IMPORTANT AMERICAN PAINTINGS, DRAWINGS AND SCULPTURE

The Properties of

MR. AND MRS. GEORGE BERMAN

THE VILLAGE OF BRONXVILLE, SOLD TO BENEFIT THE LIBRARY FUND

THE COLLECTION OF THE LATE BAYARD EWING

SOLD BY THE ORDER OF THE TRUSTEES OF THE HIRSHHORN
      MUSEUM AND SCULPTURE GARDEN, TO BENEFIT ITS ACQUISITIONS FUND

THE COLLECTION OF ROBERT S. LEE, SR.

THE LIGONIER VALLEY HISTORICAL SOCIETY, LAUGHLINTOWN, PENNSYLVANIA

THE ESTATE OF SHIRLEY POLYKOFF

THE QUEQUECHAN CLUB, FALL RIVER, MASSACHUSETTS

THE ESTATE OF LOUISE G. REEVES

THE ESTATE OF MARY W. RITCHIE, NORTH CAROLINA

THE COLLECTION OF BARBRA STREISAND

AND FROM VARIOUS SOURCES

Auction

Wednesday 2 December 1998 at 10 a.m.

502 Park Avenue at 59th Street
New York, New York 10022

Sale Code

When sending written bids or making inquiries,
this sale should be referred to as **PARK-9006**

Viewing

Friday	27 November	1.00p.m.-5.00p.m.
Saturday	28 November	10.00p.m.-5.00p.m.
Sunday	29 November	1.00p.m.-5.00p.m.
Monday	30 November	10.00a.m.-5.00p.m.
Tuesday	1 December	10.00a.m.-2.00p.m.

Christie's
502 Park Avenue at 59th Street
New York, New York 10022
Telephone: (212) 546 1000
On-line: www.christies.com

(40) Registered at the above address No. 1128160

CHRISTIE'S

CONTENTS

IMPORTANT AMERICAN PAINTINGS, DRAWINGS AND SCULPTURE

Cover illustration lot 36 (detail)
Back Cover illustration lot 30

CHRISTIE'S SPECIALISTS AND SERVICES FOR THIS SALE

For assistance and further information about this sale, please contact the following:

Specialists in American Paintings
Paul R. Provost
Head of Department (212) 546 1180
Eric P. Widing
Mia A. Schläppi
Margret K. Frame, *Cataloguer*
Sarah O'Grady, *Administrator*
Department Fax (212) 319 0858

West Coast
Catherine Leonhard (310) 385 2655

General Information
For general client assistance:

Tel: (212) 546 1010

For 24-hour recorded information on current sales and exhibitions:

Tel: (212) 371 5438

Sales Results
An international service for clients with "Touch-tone" telephones.
If you have a star (*) or a pound (#) symbol on your telephone, you can directly access our sales results to obtain sales results or to receive the faxed results of an entire sale.

New York Sales Results Line
Tel: (212) 452 4100

London Sales Results Line
Tel: (44 171) 627 2707

Absentee and Telephone Bids
For arrangement of bids for those who cannot attend the sale:

Barbara Strongin
Tel: (212) 546 1127
Fax: (212) 832 2216

Payment
For buyer assistance on terms of payment:

Vin Bissoondial
Tel: (212) 546 1040
Jennifer Galkoski
Pam Mackin
Katharine Grossmann
Tel: (212) 546 1059
Fax: (212) 317 2439
or method of payment:
Lynne Gardner
Tel: (212) 546 1124
Fax: (212) 759 7204

Shipping
For information on shipping of purchased property:

Chantal Lakatos
Tel: (212) 546 1113
Fax: (212) 980 8195

Consignor Settlements
For information on consignor payments:
Elizabeth Mitchell
Tel: (212) 546 1046
Fax: (212) 754 2390

Internet Access
For information about Christie's services and forthcoming sales:

On-line: www.christies.com

Client Advisory Services
Auction assistance for the private collector:
Tel: (212) 546 1036
      (212) 546 5824
Fax: (212) 750 1537

Kate Gubelmann (212) 546 1122
Kathy Kermian (212) 546 1126
Heads of Department

Heidi Kucker (212) 546 1031
Senior Director

Kim Solow (212) 702 2627

Jennifer Kaplan (212) 546 1074
Sharon Kim (212) 546 1074
Gabriela Lobo (212) 546 1021
Elizabeth Sarnoff (212) 546 1074
Maria Los (212) 546 1036
Mirja Spooner (212) 546 5824
Department Administrators

Ken C.Y. Yeh (212) 546 5898
Chinese Client Liaison

Shoko Suzuki (212) 546 5892
Japanese Client Liaison

Julie Kim (212) 546 5840
Korean Client Liaison

Catalogue Subscriptions
To subscribe to Christie's catalogues:
Tel: (800) 395 6300
Fax: (800) 395 5600

Outside the U.S. and Canada:
Tel: (718) 784 1480
Fax: (718) 786 0941

Christie's Auction Search Service: LotFinder™
For clients looking for something specific we have an auction search service that can notify you of items of interest to you in Christie's worldwide sales.
If you would like to register with this service, please telephone:
New York (212) 546 5851
London (44 171) 389 2963

CHRISTIE'S HISTORY

Christie's, the world's oldest fine art auctioneers, held its first auction in London on December 5, 1766.

In 1977 Christie's opened its first saleroom in America at 502 Park Avenue, followed in 1979 by Christie's East at 219 East 67th Street. In May 1997 Christie's launched a third United States saleroom – Christie's Los Angeles, 360 North Camden Drive, Beverly Hills. Today the firm is a major international company with 119 offices in 41 countries. Christie's holds sales in Britain, the United States, Australia, Hong Kong, Greece, Italy, Monaco, the Netherlands, Singapore and Switzerland. This worldwide network of salerooms enables sellers to take advantage of seasonal selling peaks, national tastes and collecting habits, and fluctuating currency exchange rates.

Over the centuries, Christie's has conducted many of the most important sales ever held. In the late 18th century the firm negotiated the sale of Sir Robert Walpole's collection to Catherine the Great who immediately installed the works in the Hermitage where many of them can be seen today. In 1794 Christie's held a five-day sale of the contents of Sir Joshua Reynolds's studio, and sold Madame du Barry's jewels in 1795, the year she was guillotined. In 1848, in a sale lasting 40 days, the firm sold the collection of the Duke of Buckingham at Stowe House.

In more recent years, Christie's in America has sold major Impressionist, Modern and Contemporary paintings from numerous renowned collections such as those of Henry Ford II, Paul Mellon, Baron Lambert, the Tremaines, Robert B. Mayer, John and Frances L. Loeb and Victor and Sally Ganz; and from distinguished Hollywood collections such as those of William and Edith Mayer Goetz, Hal B. Wallis and Billy Wilder. Other pre-eminent sales held in America include the Codex Hammer which sold for $30,800,000 – the most expensive work other than a painting ever sold, the Nicholas Brown desk and bookcase which sold for $12,100,000 – the record for American furniture, the jewels of Florence Gould and Caroline Ryan Foulke, the Estelle Doheny Library (which included Volume I of the Gutenberg Bible, sold for $5,390,000, a world record price for a printed book), and many important sales of furniture, Asian arts, porcelain, rugs, silver, stamps, wine and automobiles. In 1990, Christie's set world records for both paintings and furniture, when van Gogh's *Portrait of Dr. Gachet* sold for $82,500,000 in New York and the Badminton Cabinet reached $15,200,000 in London.

Christie's welcomes you to our viewing galleries and salerooms. Our specialists and client service staff will be pleased to help you with any aspect of buying or selling at auction.

THE BUYER

USING THIS CATALOGUE

Estimate Prices

Catalogue entries include descriptive information for every lot, as well as a price range which reflects the opinion of our specialists as to the price expected at auction. These are based upon prices recently paid at auction for comparable property and take into account condition, rarity, quality and history of previous ownership (provenance). Estimates are prepared well in advance of the sale and are subject to revision; they do not include the buyer's premium or sales tax.

Where "Estimate on Request" appears, please contact the specialist department for further information.

Reserves

The reserve is the minimum price the consignor is willing to accept and below which a lot will not be sold. This amount is confidential and will not exceed the low pre-sale estimate. Property offered for sale subject to a reserve is identified by the symbol • next to the lot number.

Conditions of Sale and Limited Warranty

If you wish to bid in a sale, we encourage you to read the **Conditions of Sale** and **Limited Warranty** which appear on the immediately following pages. The **Conditions of Sale** outline the terms governing the purchase of all property sold at auction. The **Limited Warranty** specifies the terms and conditions upon which Christie's guarantees the authenticity of property offered for sale.

Christie's Interest in Property Consigned for Sale

Christie's generally offers property consigned by others for sale at public auction. Occasionally, lots are offered which have in the course of the sale process become the property of Christie's. These lots are identified with the symbol ♦ next to the lot number. Christie's also occasionally offers for sale works owned in whole or part by an affiliate company. These lots are identified with the symbol Δ next to the lot number. On rare occasions, Christie's has a direct financial interest in lots consigned for sale. This interest may include guaranteeing a minimum price to the consignor of property or making an advance to the consignor which is secured solely by consigned property. Such lots are identified by the symbol ○ next to the lot number and are also sold subject to a reserve.

4/2/98

Buyer's Premium and Sales Tax

Buyers are reminded that the purchase price will be the sum of the final bid price plus the buyer's premium, which is generally 15% of the final bid price up to and including $50,000 and 10% of the amount above $50,000; for coins, the premium is a flat 10% of the final bid price regardless of the amount of the successful bid.

In addition to the purchase price, buyers are required to pay any sales or use tax which may be due. These charges are explained in detail under "Christie's Charges and Sales Tax" towards the end of this catalogue.

BEFORE THE AUCTION

Pre-sale viewings for all our auctions are open to the public and may be attended at no charge. All property to be auctioned is usually on view for several days prior to the sale. You are encouraged to examine lots thoroughly and to request condition reports (see below). Christie's specialists and customer service staff are available to give advice at all viewings or by appointment.

Hours of Business

Christie's Park Avenue galleries and Christie's East are open from 10 a.m. to 5 p.m. on weekdays. During the auction season there is frequent weekend viewing from 10 a.m. to 5 p.m. on Saturdays and varying afternoon hours on Sundays. The viewing schedule for each sale is published in the front of the auction catalogue.

Condition Reports

If you would like additional information on a particular lot or cannot come to the viewing, Christie's will be pleased to provide upon request a condition report. Please contact the specialist department in charge of the sale.

We remind prospective buyers that descriptions of property are not warranties and that each lot is sold "as is" in accordance with the terms of the **Limited Warranty.** Condition reports are provided as a service to interested clients, but the information furnished does not negate or modify the **Limited Warranty.** Neither Christie's nor the consignor makes any express or implied warranty or representation as to the condition of any lot offered for sale, and no statement made at any time, whether oral or written, shall constitute such a warranty or representation.

Registration

If you are planning to bid at auction, you will need to register with us. Please arrive 20 or 30 minutes before the sale to complete bidder registration and to receive a numbered paddle to identify you if you are the successful bidder. If you are a new client, or if you have not made a recent purchase at Christie's, you may be asked to supply a bank reference when you register. To avoid any delay in the release of your purchases, you may wish to prearrange check or credit approval. If so, please contact Christie's Credit Department at (212) 546 1040 or by fax at (212) 754 2390.

THE AUCTION

All auctions are open to the public, free of charge. You do not have to bid or register for a paddle. Some evening sales require an admission ticket (free, but limited in number) which must be requested in advance.

Bidding

Property is auctioned in consecutive numerical order, as it appears in the catalogue. The lot being offered is usually shown at the front of the saleroom or is illustrated on a slide screen. The auctioneer will accept bids from those present in the saleroom or absentee bidders participating by telephone or by written bid left with Christie's in advance of the auction. The auctioneer may also execute bids on behalf of the consignor to protect the reserve, either by placing consecutive bids up to the amount of the reserve or by entering bids in response to saleroom, telephone or absentee bids. Under no circumstances will the auctioneer place any bid on behalf of the consignor at or above the reserve. Nor will the auctioneer specifically identify bids placed on behalf of the consignor to protect the reserve.

Bidding Increments

Bidding generally opens below the low estimate and advances in the following increments:

$500 to $1,000	by $50
$1,000 to $2,000	by $100
$2,000 to $3,000	by $200
$3,000 to $5,000	by $200 or $200-500-800
$5,000 to $10,000	by $500
$10,000 to $20,000	by $1,000
$20,000 to $30,000	by $2,000
$30,000 to $50,000	by $2,000 or $2000-5000-8000
$50,000 to $100,000	by $5,000
$100,000 to $200,000	by $10,000
$200,000 up	Auctioneer's discretion

2/10/97

Occasionally the auctioneer may vary the increments during the course of the auction at his or her discretion.

Currency Conversion

Christie's may, as a convenience to bidders, use a currency conversion board during the auction to display the amounts being bid converted into several foreign currencies. These converted amounts are approximations only and may not represent the exact exchange rate at any given time.

Absentee Bids

If you cannot attend an auction, you may bid in other ways. The most common is the absentee bid, sometimes called an "order bid." Absentee bids are written instructions from you directing Christie's to bid for you on one or more lots up to a maximum amount you specify for each lot. Christie's staff will execute your absentee bid at the lowest possible price taking into account the reserve price and other bids. There is no charge for this service. If identical bids are left by two or more parties, the first bid received by Christie's will take preference. The auctioneer may execute bids for absentee bidders directly from the podium, clearly identifying these as order bids. Absentee Bid Forms are available in the back of every auction catalogue and also may be obtained at any Christie's location.

Telephone Bids

Christie's will also execute your bids if you cannot come to the auction and wish to participate by telephone. Arrangements should be confirmed at least one day in advance of the sale with Christie's Bid Department at (212) 546 1127. Christie's staff will execute telephone bids from designated areas in the saleroom. This service is also free of charge.

Successful Bids

The fall of the auctioneer's hammer indicates the final bid. Christie's will record the paddle number of the buyer. If your saleroom or absentee bid is successful, you will be notified immediately after the sale by mailed invoice. If you are unsuccessful, Christie's Bid Department will notify you by letter.

Unsold Lots

If a lot does not reach the reserve, it is bought-in. In other words, it remains unsold and is returned to the consignor. When the auctioneer hammers down a lot that fails to sell, he will so indicate by announcing that the lot has been "passed," "withdrawn," "returned to owner" or "bought-in."

AFTER THE AUCTION

Payment

Under normal circumstances, you are expected to pay for your purchases within seven calendar days of the sale and to remove the property you have bought by that date. Payment can be made by check, cash, money order or bank wire transfer. To avoid any delivery delays, prospective buyers are encouraged to supply bank or other suitable references before the auction.

Extended Payment Terms

With the consent of the consignor, Christie's may offer extended credit terms to prospective buyers whose creditworthiness has been verified. These terms will generally provide for the payment of the final bid price in three equal monthly installments. For further information, please contact the specialist department or Christie's Credit Department at (212) 546 1040 prior to the date of the auction.

Shipping

After payment has been made in full, Christie's may, as a service to buyers, arrange to have property packed, insured and shipped at your request and expense. For your convenience, a shipping form is enclosed with your invoice and is also available through our Art Transport Department at (212) 546 1113. In circumstances in which Christie's arranges and bills for such services via invoice or credit card, we will also include an administration charge.

We recommend that you request an estimate for any large items or property of high value requiring specialized professional packers.

Collection

Due to space constraints, Christie's often moves sold property out of the saleroom immediately after, and on occasion before, the sale. Please consult the "Pickup Information Sheet", available at the saleroom, for collection information on specific lots.

After twenty-eight calendar days from the sale, uncollected purchases will incur administration, handling and insurance charges for each day until the lots are picked up. These charges are explained in detail under **Christie's Charges and Sales Tax** at the back of this catalogue. A lot will not be released until all charges for the lot are settled.

Sale Results

Price lists are sent automatically to catalogue subscribers and absentee bidders shortly after each sale and are available to others on request. The price list will not include lots that were withdrawn or failed to sell. The price paid for any bought-in lot sold within 24 hours of the auction may be included on the list of prices realized but will be marked to indicate that such price was not realized at the auction.

In addition, interested clients can obtain spoken sale results for specific lots as well as faxed price lists for entire sales both in the United States and internationally by calling (212) 452 4100, Christie's Sales Results line.

THE CONSIGNOR

Auction Estimates

If you are considering selling your property, Christie's is happy to provide a free verbal estimate of its auction value. You can bring items into our New York salerooms at Park Avenue or Christie's East any time during normal business hours. To ensure prompt attention, it is advisable to make an appointment in advance with the specialist department. If a visit is not practical, please send a clear photograph together with dimensions and any other pertinent information that you may have.

Estate Services

Christie's Estates and Appraisals Department works closely with lawyers, bankers and others with responsibility for dispersing estates. Please call (212) 546 1060 for information about Christie's extensive estate services.

Consignment Agreement

If you decide to sell your property at auction, the procedures are simple and you should find Christie's specialists and administrative staff helpful to you throughout the process. After discussions with our specialists, you will receive a contract to sign, setting forth terms and fees for services we can provide, such as insurance, shipping and catalogue illustration. Christie's consignor commission rates are detailed on the page entitled **Christie's Charges and Sales Tax** which appears at the back of this auction catalogue.

Christie's specialists will discuss with you a suggested reserve price and our recommendations for pre-sale estimates for each piece of property you consign for sale.

Delivery of Property to Christie's

After you have consigned property to us for sale, you can either bring your property to Christie's yourself, arrange with your own shipper to deliver it to us or Christie's specialist department can organize for it to be shipped through Christie's Art Transport Department. We are always happy to assist you. For more information please contact us at (212) 546 1113. Property usually arrives at Christie's at least three months before the sale in order to allow our specialists time to research, catalogue and photograph the items. Your property is generally stored without charge at one of Christie's secure warehouses.

Financial Services

On occasion, Christie's advances funds to consignors against property consigned for sale. In certain circumstances, advances may be secured solely by the property consigned for sale. For information, please contact the specialist department to which you have consigned property or Ray Horne, Chief Financial Officer, at (212) 702 1392.

Pre-Auction Notification

Several weeks before the scheduled sale, along with thousands of Christie's worldwide subscribers, you will receive a copy of the sale catalogue in which your property is offered. You will also find enclosed with your catalogue a form indicating your property's lot numbers and confirming the reserves.

Post-Auction Notification

Within a few days after the sale, you will receive a post-sale advice listing the final bid price or, in the event that the property failed to sell, notification that it was bought-in to be returned to you. At any time during or after an auction, you can obtain the selling price for any lot by calling (212) 452 4100.

You will generally be sent payment for your sold property approximately 35 days after the sale, together with a settlement statement itemizing the selling commission and other charges.

CONDITIONS OF SALE

THESE CONDITIONS OF SALE AND LIMITED WARRANTY, TOGETHER WITH ANY GLOSSARY WHICH MAY APPEAR ON THE FOLLOWING PAGES, ARE CHRISTIE'S AND THE CONSIGNOR'S ENTIRE AGREEMENT WITH THE BUYER WITH RESPECT TO THE PROPERTY LISTED IN THIS CATALOGUE. THE CONDITIONS OF SALE AND LIMITED WARRANTY AND ALL OTHER CONTENTS OF THIS CATALOGUE MAY BE AMENDED BY POSTED NOTICES OR ORAL ANNOUNCEMENTS MADE DURING THE SALE. THE PROPERTY WILL BE OFFERED BY US AS AGENT FOR THE CONSIGNOR, UNLESS THE CATALOGUE INDICATES OTHERWISE. BY BIDDING AT AUCTION, YOU AGREE TO BE BOUND BY THESE TERMS AND CONDITIONS.

1. The authenticity of the authorship of property listed in the catalogue is guaranteed only as stated in the Limited Warranty and otherwise all property is sold "AS IS" without any representations or warranties by us or the Consignor as to merchantability, fitness for a particular purpose, description, size, quality, rarity, importance, medium, provenance, exhibition history, literature or historical relevance of any property. No statement set forth in this catalogue or made at the auction or in the bill of sale or otherwise, whether oral or written, shall be deemed such a warranty, representation or assumption of liability. We and the Consignor make no representations and warranties, express or implied, as to whether the purchaser acquires any copyrights for any reproduction rights in any property. Neither we nor the Consignor are responsible for errors and omissions in the catalogue, glossary or any supplemental material.

2. The purchase price payable by a buyer will be the sum of the final bid price plus the buyer's premium, together with any applicable sales or compensating use tax. The buyer's premium is 15% of the final bid price up to and including $50,000 plus 10% of any amount in excess of $50,000.

3. We reserve the right to withdraw any property before or at the sale and shall have no liability whatsoever for such withdrawal.

4. We reserve the right to reject any bid. The highest bidder acknowledged by the auctioneer will be the buyer. In the event of any dispute between bidders, or any other issue with respect to the bidder, the auctioneer will have absolute discretion to determine the successful bidder, to continue the bidding, to cancel the sale or to reoffer and resell the article in dispute. If any dispute arises after the sale, our sale record is conclusive.

5. Although in our discretion we will execute absentee bids (written bids left with us prior to sale) or accept telephone bids as a convenience to clients who are not present at auction, we are not responsible for failing to execute such bids or for any errors or omissions in connection therewith.

6. Each lot marked with ● next to the lot number is offered subject to a reserve, which is the confidential minimum price below which the lot will not be sold. Christie's shall act to protect the reserve by bidding through the auctioneer. The auctioneer may open bidding on any lot below the reserve by placing a bid on behalf of the Consignor. The auctioneer may continue to bid on behalf of the Consignor up to the amount of the reserve, either by placing consecutive bids or by placing bids in response to other bidders.

7. Title to the offered lot passes to the buyer upon the fall of the auctioneer's hammer and the announcement by the auctioneer that the lot has been sold, subject to compliance by the buyer with all other Conditions of Sale. The buyer assumes full risk and responsibility for the lot and shall immediately pay the full purchase price or such part as we, in our sole discretion, require. In addition, the buyer may be required to sign a confirmation of purchase. We reserve the right to impose a late charge of 16% per annum of the total purchase price if payment is not made in accordance with this paragraph.

8. No lot may be removed from our premises until the buyer has paid the purchase price in full or has satisfied such terms as we, in our sole discretion, shall require. Subject to the foregoing, all lots are to be paid for no later than 4:30 p.m. on the seventh calendar day following the sale. We may move the property to an off-site warehouse at the risk of the buyer. If a lot has not been collected by 4:30 p.m. of the twenty-eighth calendar day following the sale, the buyer will be liable for administration, handling and insurance charges of at least $30 for each lot so remaining. These charges will increase each day, up to an additional $20 per day per lot, until the lot is collected, and must be settled in full before the lot will be released.

9. We are not responsible for our acts or omissions in the handling, packing or shipping of purchased lots or those of other handlers, packers or carriers of purchased lots. Packing and handling of purchased lots are at the entire risk of the buyer. If Christie's arranges and bills for such services via invoice or credit card, Christie's will include an administration charge. If we obtain on behalf of the purchaser an export license for an item containing an endangered species, there will be a charge of $150 for each license obtained.

10. If the buyer fails to comply with any of these Conditions of Sale, we may, in addition to asserting all remedies available by law, including the right to hold such defaulting buyer liable for the purchase price, (i) cancel the sale, retaining as liquidated damages any payment made by the buyer, (ii) resell the property without reserve at public auction or privately on seven days' notice to the buyer, (iii) pay the Consignor an amount equal to the net proceeds payable in respect of the amount bid by the defaulting buyer and then resell the property to a third party without reserve at public auction or privately on seven days' notice to such buyer or (iv) take such other action as we deem necessary or appropriate. If we resell the property pursuant to clause (ii) or (iii) above, the defaulting buyer shall be liable for the payment of any deficiency between the purchase price and the price obtained upon resale pursuant to clause (ii) or (iii) above and all costs and expenses, including administration, handling, insurance, warehousing, the expenses of both

sales, reasonable attorneys' fees, commissions, incidental damages and all other charges due hereunder. In the event that such buyer pays a portion of the purchase price for any or all lots purchased, we shall apply the payment received to such lot or lots that we, in our sole discretion, deem appropriate. Any buyer who fails to comply with these Conditions of Sale will be deemed to have granted us a security interest in, and we may retain as collateral security for such buyer's obligation to us, any property in our possession owned by such buyer. We shall have the benefit of all rights of a secured party under the Uniform Commercial Code adopted in the state where the auction is held.

11. The respective rights and obligations of the parties with respect to the Conditions of Sale and the conduct of the auction shall be governed and interpreted by the laws of the state in which the auction is held. By bidding at an auction, whether present in person or by agent, by absentee bid, telephone or other means, the buyer shall be deemed to have consented to the exclusive jurisdiction of the courts of such state and the Federal courts sitting in such state. The buyer expressly agrees that (i) neither we nor the Consignor shall be liable, in whole or in part, for any special, indirect or consequential damages, including, without limitation, loss of profits and (ii) the buyer's damages are limited exclusively to the original purchase price paid for the lot.

LIMITED WARRANTY

Christie's warrants the authenticity of authorship on the terms and conditions and to the extent set forth herein. Subject to the provisions of the last paragraph hereof, Christie's warrants for a period of five years from the date of sale that any property described in headings printed in UPPER CASE TYPE in

this catalogue (as such description may be amended by any saleroom notice or announcement) which is unqualifiedly stated to be the work of a named author or authorship, is authentic and not counterfeit. The term "author" or "authorship" refers to the creator of the property or to the period, culture, source or origin, as the case may be, with which the creation of such property is identified in the description of the property in this catalogue. Only UPPER CASE TYPE headings of lots in this catalogue (i.e., headings having capital-letter type) indicate the degree of authenticity of authorship warranted by Christie's. If this catalogue has a glossary, the terms used in such headings are further explained therein. **Any heading which is stated in the Glossary to represent a qualified opinion is not subject to the warranty contained herein. Christie's warranty does not apply to supplemental material which appears below the UPPER CASE TYPE heading of each lot in this catalogue and Christie's is not responsible for any errors or omissions in such supplemental material.**

The benefits of this warranty are not assignable and shall be applicable only to the original buyer of the lot and not subsequent assigns, purchasers, heirs, owners or others who have or may acquire an interest therein. This warranty is conditioned upon the buyer returning the lot to Christie's, 502 Park Avenue, New York, N.Y. 10022, in the same condition as at the time of sale.

The buyer's sole and exclusive remedy against Christie's and the seller under this warranty shall be the rescission of the sale and the refund of the original purchase price paid for the lot. This remedy shall be in lieu of any other remedy which might otherwise be available as a matter of law, and neither Christie's nor the seller shall be liable, in whole or in part, for any special, incidental or consequential damages, including, without limitation, loss of profits.

Except as otherwise specifically provided herein, all property is sold "as is" and neither Christie's nor the seller makes any express or implied warranty or representation of any kind or nature with respect to the property. In no event shall Christie's or the seller be responsible for the correctness of, or be deemed to have made, any representation or warranty of merchantability, fitness for purpose, description, size, medium, genuineness, attribution, provenance or condition concerning the property, and no statement set forth in this catalogue or made at the sale or in the bill of sale or invoice or elsewhere, whether oral or written, shall be deemed such a warranty or representation or an assumption of liability. However, the foregoing disclaimer of implied warranties does not apply to articles produced after July 3, 1975. **Christie's and the seller make no warranty or representation, express or implied, that the buyer of any work of art or other property will acquire any copyright or reproduction rights thereto.**

Christie's limited warranty does not apply to the (i) attribution of authorship of paintings, drawings, graphic art or sculpture created before 1870, unless such works are determined to be counterfeit, as such attribution is based on current scholarly opinion, which may change, (ii) attribution of authorship of paintings, drawings, graphic art or sculpture created after 1870 if such attribution at the date of the auction was in accordance with then generally accepted scholarly opinion or fairly indicated there to be a conflict of such opinion or (iii) identification of the period or dates of the execution of any property which may be proven inaccurate by means of a scientific process which was not generally accepted for use until after the date of the auction, unreasonably expensive or impractical to use or likely to have caused damage to the property.

EXPLANATION OF CATALOGUING PRACTICE

FOR PICTURES, DRAWINGS, PRINTS
AND MINIATURES

Terms used in this catalogue have
the meanings ascribed to them
below. Please note that all
statements in this catalogue as to
Authorship are made subject to the
provisions of the CONDITIONS
OF SALE and LIMITED
WARRANTY.

1. GILBERT STUART
   In Christie's opinion a work by the
   artist.

2. Attributed to GILBERT
      STUART*
   In Christie's qualified opinion a
   work of the period of the artist
   which may be in whole or part the
   work of the artist.

3. School of GILBERT STUART*
   In Christie's qualified opinion a
   work by a pupil or follower of the
   artist.

4. Manner of GILBERT STUART*
   In Christie's qualified opinion a
   work in the style of the artist,
   possibly of a later period.

5. After GILBERT STUART*
   In Christie's qualified opinion a
   copy of the work of the artist.

6. 'signed'
   Has a signature which in Christie's
   qualified opinion is the signature of
   the artist.

7. 'bears signature'
   Has a signature which in Christie's
   qualified opinion might be the
   signature of the artist.

8. 'dated'
   Is so dated and in Christie's
   qualified opinion was executed at
   about that date.

9. 'bears date'
   Is so dated and in Christie's qualified
   opinion may have been executed at
   about that date.

*This term and its definition in this
Explanation of Cataloguing Practice
are a qualified statement as to
Authorship. While the use of this term
is based upon careful study and
represents the opinion of experts,
Christie's and the consignor assume no
risk, liability and responsibility for the
authenticity of authorship of any lot in
this catalogue described by this term.

Sales Tax Notice

*Christie's is offering lots 15 and 94
in this catalogue as agent for an
organization holding a State of New
York Exempt Organization Certificate.
Accordingly, no sales tax is due on the
purchase price of the lot if the property
is picked up or delivered in the State of
New York. However, a compensating
use tax is due from the buyer if any
such lot is shipped to New Jersey or
Connecticut or any of the following
states where Christie's maintains
offices: Alabama, California, Florida,
Illinois, Massachusetts, Pennsylvania,
Rhode Island, Texas and
Washington, D.C.

© Christie's Inc. (1994)

Important Notice

★Christie's warranty of authenticity
near the front of this catalogue does
not apply to works executed before
1870. Accordingly, Christie's and
Seller assume no risk or responsibility
for the authenticity for the following
lots: 1, 6,57, 62, 63, 64, 67, and 69.

EXPLANATION OF CATALOGUING PRACTICE

For Sculpture

Terms used in this catalogue have the meanings ascribed to them below. Please note that all statements in this catalogue as to Authorship are made subject to the provisions of the CONDITIONS OF SALE and LIMITED WARRANTY.

1. AUGUSTUS SAINT-GAUDENS
    (artist's first name or names and his last name)
    In our opinion a work by the artist. In the case of a bronze or other multiple, the work has been cast with the artist's consent or that of his estate either during his lifetime or shortly thereafter. In the case of a marble, wood or other hand carved medium, the work has been carved by the artist or by his studio under his supervision.

2. Attributed to AUGUSTUS SAINT-GAUDENS*
    In our qualified opinion, a work of the period of the artist which may be the work of the artist as described previously.

3. After AUGUSTUS SAINT-GAUDENS*
    In our qualified opinion, a later unauthorized copy after a work by the artist and not directly connected in any way with the artist, his studio or estate.

*This term and its definition in this Explanation of Cataloguing Practice are a qualified statement as to Authorship. While the use of this term is based upon careful study and represents the opinion of experts, Christie's and the consignor assume no risk, liability and responsibility for the authenticity of authorship of any lot in this catalogue described by this term.

PLEASE NOTE THIS IMPORTANT CHANGE IN CATALOGUING PRACTICE

In Christie's U.S.A. catalogues, only catalogue descriptions of multiple works (such as prints, coins, stamps and wine) include reference to condition. For all other types of property, no statement of condition is made and only alterations or replacements of components are listed. Condition reports are available upon request. Please contact the specialists in charge of the sale.

1

•1

JOHN JAMES AUDUBON* (1785-1851)

Eastern Bluebird

signed and dated 'Audubon 1827' (lower center)

watercolor and pencil on paper

13 x 10 in. (33 x 25.4 cm.)

RELATED WORKS:

Eastern Bluebird, watercolor, pastel, gouache and graphite on paper, 18⅞ x 11⅚ in. (47.9 x 30.3 cm.), New-York Historical Society, New York

John James Audubon, foremost American naturalist of the nineteenth century, "made the affectionate notations in his journal about the [Eastern Bluebird], declaring: 'It adds to the delight imparted by spring, and enlivens the dull days of winter. Full of innocent vivacity, warbling its ever pleasant notes, and familiar as any bird can be in its natural freedom, it is one of the most agreeable of our feathered favorites.'" (A. Blaugrund and T. Stebbins, Jr., eds., *John James Audubon: The Watercolors for The Birds of America*, New York, 1993, p. 96)

Estimate: $60,000-80,000

2

•2

WILLIAM BRADFORD (1823-1892)
Labrador Fishing Boats Near Cape Charles
signed 'Wm. Bradford NY' (lower right)—inscribed with
title on the stretcher
oil on canvas
18 x 30 in. (45.7 x 76.2 cm.)

Estimate: $40,000-60,000

3

VARIOUS PROPERTIES

•3

WILLIAM TROST RICHARDS (1833-1905)
Off the Coast of Rhode Island
signed and dated 'Wm T. Richards. 1874.'(lower right)
pencil and gouache on paper
8¾ x 13½ in. (22.3 x 34.2 cm.)

PROVENANCE:
Martha Rhodes, Rockport, Maine.

Estimate: $20,000-30,000

4

•4

MARTIN JOHNSON HEADE (1819-1904)

Still Life with Red and Pink Roses

signed 'M. J. Heade' (lower left)

oil on board

14 x 12in. (35.6 x 30.5cm.)

A letter from Dr. Theodore E. Stebbins, Jr. accompanies the lot.

This painting will be included in Theodore E. Stebbins, Jr.'s forthcoming revised *catalogue raisonné* of Heade's work.

Estimate: $50,000-70,000

5

•5

SEVERIN ROESEN (1815-*circa* 1872)
Strawberries and Porcelain
signed 'S. Roesen' (lower right)
oil on canvas
25 x 30in. (63.5 x 76.2cm.)

PROVENANCE:
Marie and Jacob Zins, Chatham, New Jersey
Beatrice J. Feins, Springfield, New Jersey
By descent in the family to the present owner

A letter dated July 26, 1998 from Dr. Judith O'Toole discussing
this work accompanies the lot.

Estimate: $70,000–100,000

•6

FREDERIC EDWIN CHURCH★ (1826-1900)

Bee Craft Mountain from Church's Farm

signed and dated 'F.E. Church 67' (lower center)—numbered '32' on the stretcher
oil on canvas stretched over panel
15 x 24 in. (38.1 x 61 cm.)

PROVENANCE:
Robert W. deForest, New York, possibly acquired directly from the artist.
Innis Young, Poughkeepsie, New York, purchased from the above, 1936.
Walter Wallace, New York.

RELATED WORKS:
Bee Craft Mountain from Church's Farm, graphite and gouache on light green paper, 11⅟₁₆ x 16⅜ in. (28.1 x 41.1 cm.), Olana State Historic Site, Hudson, New York

Frederic Edwin Church painted *Bee Craft Mountain from Church's Farm* in 1867, seven years after he purchased farmland near Hudson, New York from Levi Simmons, a local farmer. The property, known as 'Church's Farm,' would become the site of the artist's celebrated home, Olana.

James Anthony Ryan writes, "From the beginning, Church hoped that 'the farm' as the family called it, would serve as a retreat from an often-painful artistic celebrity. Painting at first in the cottage or in an outbuilding, Church erected a large wood-frame studio in 1864 at the topmost boundary of his property on Long Hill. He no doubt chose this location as it offered the site's broadest panoramas, which he depicted on paper and canvas many times between 1861 and the 1890s. 'I am appalled when I look at the magnificent scenery that encircles my clumsy studio, and then glance at the painted oil-cloth on my easel,' Church wrote to art critic Henry Tuckerman in 1867." (*Frederic Edwin Church*, Washington, DC, 1989, p. 129)

The Hudson River Valley had deep personal meaning for Church. From his earliest days as an artist in the studio of Thomas Cole, Church was inspired by the landscape of the area, and his love for it continued over the course of his lifetime. *Bee Craft Mountain from Church's Farm* reflects this close relationship between the artist and the natural landscape that inspired him early in his career and that would become his permanent home.

An extant sketch dated August 1863 in the collection of the Olana State Historic Site relates closely to *Bee Craft Mountain from Church's Farm*. The identical outline of Bee Craft Mountain, located to the east from the northeastern boundary of Church's Farm, appears silhouetted against the light-filled sky in *Bee Craft Mountain from Church's Farm*. However the foreground and middleground of the painting are quite different from those in the drawing— an indication that the artist departed from purely topographical renderings to create works of art with more powerful personal associations. *Bee Craft Mountain from Church's Farm* exemplifies this approach to landscape painting, as it embodies the special and nearly spiritual relationship between the artist and the land that would become his home.

Bee Craft Mountain from Church's Farm may have served as a particular reminder of the artist's close association with the land that became so important to him and his family. The painting depicts the topography that Church saw regularly as he traveled to the town of Hudson. The view in the drawing of 1863 and in the painting of 1867 also represents "an overview of his accomplishments as a gentleman farmer after three years' residency. . . Forty-one months after the birth of his first child, he looked toward his farm and the blue mountains he often had sketched as Thomas Cole's student, and felt himself a part of the landscape" (Gerald L. Carr, *Frederic Edwin Church: Catalogue Raisonné© of Works of Art at Olana State Historic Site*, vol. I, Cambridge, England, 1994, p. 288)

Like many of Church's finest paintings, *Bee Craft Mountain from Church's Farm* is filled with a powerful and serene sense of American light and space. The clouds in the distant sky are highlighted with delicate touches of pink—a technique the artist learned from his teacher and founder of the Hudson River School, Thomas Cole. Other elements in the painting are hallmarks of Church's mature style of landscape painting. For example, the artists has included touches of crimson in the flowering shrubs in the lower right corner. In addition, the middleground surrounding the water is filled with lush trees and grasses painted in deep greens. Just as the land and vegetation is rendered with great care, so too does Church depict the sky and atmosphere with great sensitivity. The moon in the center distance provides a cool, spiritual light as its reflection sparkles on the surface of the water in the middle distance. The overall effect gives the composition a radiance that ranks *Bee Craft Mountain from Church's Farm* as a masterwork of Hudson River School painting.

Bee Craft Mountain from Church's Farm has a highly distinguished history of ownership, as it belonged to the earliest patrons and collectors of American paintings. *Bee Craft Mountain from Church's Farm* hung in Robert W. de Forest's New York home on Washington Square North. In 1872 de Forest, who would serve as president of the Metropolitan Museum of Art from 1913-31, married Emily Johnston, the daughter of John Taylor Johnston, a founder and first president of the Metropolitan in 1870. John Taylor Johnston was an active patron and collector of Hudson River School paintings. A friend and patron of Frederic Edwin Church, Johnston was a member of the Union League Club, as was the artist. Keenly interested in American art, a love nurtured in part through John Taylor Johnston, Edwin W. de Forest and his wife, Emily Johnston de Forest, were the donors of the American Wing to the Metropolitan Museum.

Estimate: $250,000-350,000

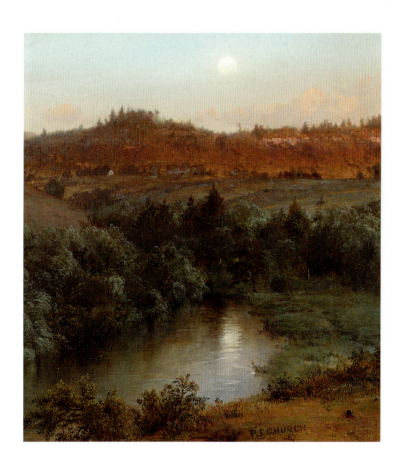

7

•7

WILLIAM HOLBROOK BEARD (1823-1900)
So You Wanna Get Married, Eh?
signed and dated 'W.H. Beard 1886' (lower left)
oil on canvas
24 x 18 in. (61 x 45.7 cm.)

PROVENANCE:
The Robert P. Coggins Collection, Marietta, Georgia.

EXHIBITED:
Rochester, New York, Memorial Art Gallery, University of
Rochester, *Selections from the Robert P. Coggins Collection of American
Painting*, February-April 1977, p. 19, illustrated (This exhibition
also traveled to: Atlanta, Georgia, High Museum of Art,
December 1976-January 1977; Ithaca, New York, Herbert F.
Johnson Museum of Art, Cornell University, May-June 1977)
Decatur, Georgia, Dana Fine Arts Building, Agnes Scott College,
American Paintings from the Robert P. Coggins Collection, October-
December 1978, no. 40

Estimate: $40,000-60,000

20

35

7A

•7A

SANFORD ROBINSON GIFFORD (1823-1880)
Sunset in the White Mountains
oil on canvas
5½ x 10⅜ in. (14 x 26.3 cm.)
A letter from Ila Weiss accompanies the lot.

Estimate: $30,000-50,000

PROPERTY OF A TEXAS PRIVATE COLLECTION

•8

THOMAS MORAN (1837-1926)
Pool in the Forest, Long Island
signed and dated 'TMoran 83' (lower left)
oil on panel
14 x 12¼ in. (35.6 x 31.1 cm.)

PROVENANCE:
John Levy Galleries, New York.
M.R. Schweitzer Gallery, New York.

This painting will be included in Stephen L. Good's and Phyllis Braff's forthcoming *catalogue raisonné* of the artist's work.

Estimate: $70,000-100,000

8

9

PROPERTY OF
A NEW HAMPSHIRE PRIVATE COLLECTION

•9

DANIEL RIDGWAY KNIGHT (1839-1924)

Julia Among the Roses

signed and inscribed 'Ridgway Knight Paris' (lower right)
oil on canvas
46 x 35 in. (116.8 x 88.9 cm.)

PROVENANCE:
M. Knoedler, & Co., New York.
Frank P. Carpenter, Manchester, New Hampshire, acquired from
the above in 1908.
By descent in the family to the present owner.

This work retains its original hand-carved Walfred Thulin frame,
signed 'Thulin.'

Estimate: $80,000–120,000

10

PROPERTY OF A PRIVATE COLLECTOR

•10

THOMAS MORAN (1837-1926)
Venice—Grand Canal
signed and dated 'TMoran 1912' (lower right)
oil on canvas
30 x 40in. (76.2 x 101.6cm.)

PROVENANCE:
Ehrich-Newhouse, Inc., New York, (possibly).
The Milch Galleries, New York.

This painting will be included in Stephen L. Good's and Phyllis Braff's forthcoming *catalogue raisonné* of the artist's work.

Estimate: $80,000-120,000

PROPERTY OF A EUROPEAN LADY

•11

FREDERICK CARL FRIESEKE (1874-1939)

Cherry Blossoms

signed 'F.C. Frieseke' (lower left)

oil on canvas

32½ x 26¼ in. (82.6 x 66.6 cm.)

A classic work in the Impressionist manner, Frederick Carl Frieseke's *Cherry Blossoms* is a magnificent example of the artist's mature style. Executed circa 1914, during one of the most prominent points of the artist's career, Frieseke had the comfort of a solid reputation that "had been well established through an impressive series of honors which came early and steadily." (M.M. Domit, *Frederick Frieseke, 1874-1939*, Savannah, Georgia, 1974, p. 10)

Although he lived in Giverny, France in the early years of the twentieth century, Frieseke never considered himself a French Impressionist. He declared: "I am not an expatriate. I often return to the states, and I look forward to finally locating there. I stay on here because I am more free to and there are not the Puritanical restrictions which prevail in America... I can paint a nude in my own garden or down by the fish pond and not be run out of town." (*Frederick Frieseke*, 1874-1939, p. 10)

Indeed, the artist's nudes are among the finest expressions of American Impressionism. Moussa M. Domit notes: "Frieseke's real and most consistent interest from the beginning seems to have been in painting the nude or draped figure, especially 'in sunshine' or in dappled shade of trees, or under an umbrella but also in the delicate light of indoors. Clearly his reputation in Europe was mainly as a painter of nudes. German and Italian, as well as French, critical interest centered on this aspect of his work, and writers were unanimous in praising his skills." (*Frederick Frieseke*, 1874-1939, p. 12)

This painting will be inlcuded in the forthcoming *catalogue raisonné* of Frieseke's work being compiled by Nicholas Kilmer, the artist's grandson.

Estimate: $350,000-450,000

11

•12

THEODORE ROBINSON (1852-1896)

Girl Raking Hay

signed 'Th. Robinson' (lower left)

oil on canvas

18½ x 15½ in. (47 x 39.3 cm.)

PROVENANCE:

Vose Galleries, Boston, Massachusetts.

George D. Pratt.

Sale: American Art Association, Pratt Sale, January 16, 1937, no. 358.

William T. Cresmer, Glencoe, Illinois.

Sale: Nanzel Gallery, William T. Cresmer Collection, September 17, 1961, no. 132, illustrated

Hirschl & Adler Galleries, Inc., New York.

Meredith Long and Company, Houston, Texas.

Private Collection, Houston, Texas.

Christie's, New York, May 29, 1987, lot 162.

Acquired by the present owner from the above.

EXHIBITED:

Brooklyn, New York, The Brooklyn Museum, *Theodore Robinson, 1852-1896*, November 1946-January 1947, no. 79

New York, Hirschl & Adler Galleries, Inc., *Important Recent Acquisitions*, February 1972, no. 63, illustrated

Of the many American painters drawn to the French village of Giverny, Theodore Robinson developed perhaps the most significant relationship with the master of Impressionism, Claude Monet. Robinson's paintings, such as *Girl Raking Hay*, which he executed during his residency in Giverny from 1888-1892, rank among the most enduring achievements of American Impressionism.

During his years in Giverny, Robinson developed a sophisticated Impressionist technique in both landscapes and figural compositions. Whereas the landscapes of the fields around Giverny and neighboring villages are rendered with tighter, crisper brushstrokes, his figural works of 1890-92 display his Impressionist style at its freest and most spontaneous. In paintings such as *Girl Raking Hay*, most likely executed in the summer of 1890, Robinson often placed the figure in the context of meadows, woods, or fields—quiet, light-filled spaces that evoke the peacefulness and tranquility of the unspoiled countryside. These outdoor spaces also allowed Robinson to concentrate on the effects of sunlight and color as it filtered through trees or was reflected off the surface of a rushing, gurgling brook. Like many of the American painters living in Giverny, Robinson relied on local residents to pose for his canvases. The model for *Girl Raking Hay* is Josephine Trognon, a Giverny peasant whom Robinson painted a number of times during the summer of 1890.

Robinson acquired a thorough understanding of the Impressionist work of Claude Monet, yet the American painter was not merely an imitator of the French master. Robinson absorbed Monet's theories and built on them to create works that reflected his personal style of Impressionism. Sona Johnston has written, "He did not abstract the image before him as Monet had advised. With few exceptions his forms remain solid, firmly-defined, and the subject matter is always clearly identifiable. Although the degree of his initial devotion to Monet's Impressionism is obvious, his art demonstrates a selection and subsequent interpretation of these elements most sympathetic to his manner of expression." (*Theodore Robinson*, Baltimore, Maryland, 1973, p. xiv.)

Unlike some American Impressionist painters working in Giverny who painted with bold palettes in strong primary colors, Theodore Robinson developed careful color harmonies that were exceptionally refined. *Girl Raking Hay* reveals how the artist composed the picture with a sensitive eye to the complexities of softer hues and half tones. Various hues of greens and pinks are modulated against one another and vivid touches of white are dabbed to enliven the surface.

Robinson received positive critical response for his approach to the Impressionist style. Several years before he painted *Girl Raking Hay* a critic wrote in the *Art Amateur*, "Mr. Robinson is one of those who have really gained a good deal in the study of impressionist methods. . . the narrowing of his aim in this case, as in so many others has been the saving of the artist." And in 1893 the *Art Amateur* again praised his work: "Impressionism has many exponents, but no one else that appears to be so sure of himself or of his method as Mr. Theodore Robinson." And more than a decade after Robinson's death, the critic Christian Brinton praised the artist's canvases, calling them "radiant masterpieces" and writing, "The pioneer American Impressionist painted modest themes—bits of winding canal, glimpses of white cottage nestled against green hillside, peasant girls musing upon the grass. There is no pose, no hint of pretense here, Robinson went straight to the heart of the scene, however simple, and unambitious it may have seemed. Out of little he made much. He painted light, air and colour. The purest lyric talent we have thus far produced, he sang a song steeped in outdoor brightness and objective tranquility." ("American Painting at the Panama-Pacific Exposition," *International Studio*, August 1915, p. 30)

Unlike some American Impressionist painters working in Giverny who painted with bold palettes in strong primary colors, Theodore Robinson developed careful color harmonies that were exceptionally refined. *Girl Raking Hay* reveals how the artist composed the picture with a sensitive eye to the complexities of softer hues and half tones. Various hues of greens and pinks are modulated against one another and vivid touches of white are dabbed to enliven the surface.

Estimate: $400,000-600,000

12

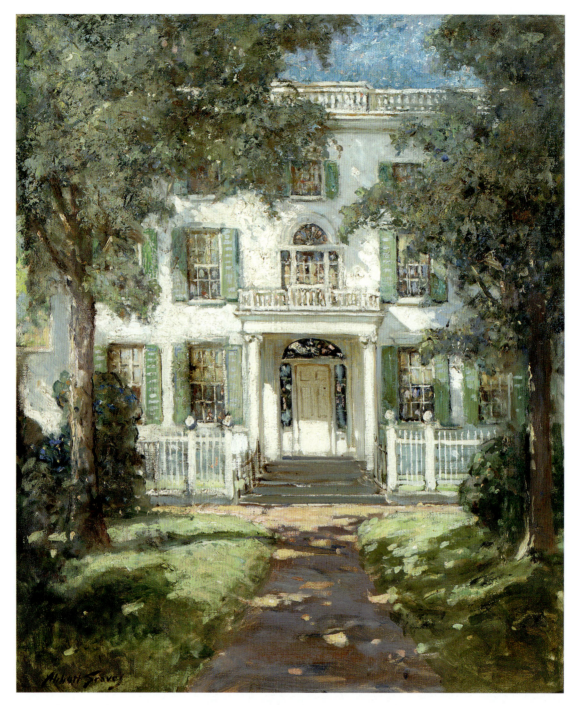

13

PROPERTY FROM
A PRIVATE COLLECTION, NEW YORK

•13

ABBOTT FULLER GRAVES (1859-1936)
Federal House, Wiscasset, Maine
signed 'Abbott Graves' (lower left)
oil on canvas
30¼ x 25 in. (76.8 x 63.5 cm.)

Estimate: $50,000-70,000

14

ANOTHER PROPERTY

•14

CHILDE HASSAM (1859-1935)

Trees, New Hampshire

signed and dated 'Childe Hassam 1912' (lower right)
oil on canvas
20 x 30 in. (50.8 x 76.2 cm.)

PROVENANCE:
Hirschl & Adler Galleries, Inc., New York.

In 1889 Hassam returned from his travels in Europe where he first encountered paintings by the French Impressionists which had great influence on his art. "During his stay in Europe his brushwork became freer as light and color became his major interest." (Hirschl & Adler Galleries, Inc., *Childe Hassam, 1859-1935*, New York, 1964) Not unlike many famous French Impressionists, Hassam painted several series from the same locale to illustrate the influences and aspects of light and color in a particular scene.

As an American born artist, Childe Hassam felt his American heritage was extremely important and during his lifetime a great deal of subject matter was taken from everyday scenes of American life and from various American settings. The New England coast and surrounding countryside were particular favorites for Childe Hassam. In September of 1911 he spent some time in Rockingham, New Hampshire, where he may have encountered a scene very much like the landscape depicted in *Trees, New Hampshire*.

Trees, New Hampshire, executed one year later, is a splendid example of the New England countryside with its summer scene of tree groupings and coastal ponds under an expanse of a cloud-filled sky. This beautiful Impressionistic piece, with Hassam's uniquely broken but controlled brushwork, captures the mood of lush greenery and a coastal climate typical of New Hampshire.

This painting will be included in Stuart P. Feld's and Kathleen M. Burnside's forthcoming *catalogue raisonné* of the artist's work.

Estimate: $100,000-150,000

•15

CHILDE HASSAM (1859-1935)

Central Park

signed and inscribed 'Childe Hassam N.Y.' (lower left)

oil on canvas

18 x 22½in. (45.7 x 56.1cm.)

PROVENANCE:
William F. Burt, Bronxville, New York.
Gift to the present owner from the above, 1947.

EXHIBITED:
New York, New Society of Artists, *Second Annual Exhibition*, November 1920, no. 59
New York, Hirschl & Adler Galleries, Inc., *The Artist in the Park: A Benefit Exhibition for The Central Park Conservatory*, April-May 1980, no. 50
New York, Jordan-Volpe Gallery, *Childe Hassam: American Impressionist*, May-July 1994

LITERATURE:
W.H. Gerdts, *Impressionist New York*, New York, 1994, p. 134, illus.

Childe Hassam's images of New York City from the 1890s are among the most poignant and brilliant examples of American Impressionism. The success of Hassam's urban views from the late nineteenth century is attributed to his love of observing the vitality of city life and the artist's unique style of composition, color, light and atmosphere.

Hassam recorded various locations throughout the city during this time, including a series of works celebrating Central Park. Central Park at the end of the 19th century was the grandest and most renowned public park in the nation. Located in the center of Manhattan, it spanned over eight hundred acres of rolling hills, meadows and forests dotted with ponds and lakes and dissected by miles of walking, equestrian and carriage paths. At its opening in the late 1850s, the park provided a much needed escape for an urban population that was suffering under the burden of rapid industrialization. Central Park achieved emblematic status and came to embody the nation's antidote for the encroaching modern world. Hassam's portrayal of this landmark, *Central Park* from *circa* 1890-92, illustrates the brilliance of American Impressionism and extols the beauty and sanctuary of this manmade oasis amidst the chaos of a changing world.

Hassam's urban experience began as early as 1885 in the city of Boston where he moved after his marriage to Kathleen Maude Doan. Exploring Boston's fashionable west end by the Charles River inspired Hassam to begin portraying modern city life. In 1886 Hassam moved to Paris for three years where his continued interest in urban life focused on the famous bustling boulevards and parks, capturing the comings and goings of the city's elite populace. Recognizing the prominence of New York as an international art center, Hassam relocated to the city in the winter of 1889. The artist first settled into a studio at 95 Fifth Avenue at Seventeenth Street where he was quickly enthralled by the cultural vitality and cosmopolitan aires of the city. His enthusiasm was recounted to an interviewer in 1892: "I believe the thoroughfares of the great French metropolis are not one whit more interesting than the streets of New York. There are days here when the sky and atmosphere are exactly those of Paris, and when the squares and parks are every bit as beautiful in color and grouping." (H.B. Weinberg, D. Bolger and D.P. Curry, *American Impressionism and Realism*, New York, 1994, p. 179) Hassam's passion for the city immediately found direct expression in the canvases he produced and critics quickly came to associate the artist with New York. Later in 1895, one critic would hail Hassam as "a brilliant painter, a sort of Watteau of the boulevards, with unlimited spark and gaiety, movement and animation. He suggests a crowd well; he gives you the color of the streets and the tone of the city." (W.H. Howe and G. Torrey, "Childe Hassam," *Art Interchange* 34, May 1895, p. 133)

Hassam remained at this studio on lower Fifth Avenue for the next two years and then moved in 1892 to the Chelsea Hotel at 222 West 23rd Street where he would reside for about a year. Lower Fifth Avenue had been in earlier years considered very fashionable, but by the time Hassam moved to this area it had transformed into a more commercial district. The city's extremely wealthy had migrated further uptown on Fifth Avenue near Central Park. Spanning from about Fiftieth Street to Eightieth Street, this area along the park was commonly referred to as "Millionaires' Row" with the construction throughout the 1870s and 1880s of great mansions and luxury apartment buildings. As one critic noted: "The fashionable life of the metropolis once had its center here [lower Fifth Avenue], and although the neighborhood still retains much of its old-time character, and nothing of natural beauty seems lacking to make it desirable as a residence, the tide of fashion has receded northward... ." (E. Idell Zeisloft, *The New Metropolis*, New York, 1899, p. 494, as quoted in W.H. Gerdts, *Impressionist New York*, New York, 1994, p. 46)

15

Hassam throughout the 1890s explored and painted areas in and around Fifth Avenue, one of the most famous and diverse thoroughfares in the country. One writer observed: "In the entire length Fifth Avenue is not one thing, but everything—a symbol, a compendium, a cross section of the national life... It is a study in progressive sociology with mansions and factories, libraries, museums, vacant lots, hospitals, parks and slums. While other streets have their own characters as well as length....Fifth Avenue alone has significance." (S. Strunsky, "The Lane That Has No Turning," *Harper's New Monthly Magazine* 131, September 1915, p. 490 as quoted in *Impressionist New York*, p. 45-46) Hassam devoted most of his paintings to bustling and buggy filled streets and squares, yet his images of public parks located in close proximity to Fifth Avenue compliment and complete the artist's vision of the city during this time. Central Park, the most famous of public parks, was the subject for some of the artist most acclaimed works. *Central Park* from *circa* 1890-92 is one such example.

In *Central Park*, Hassam found a subject worthy of his considerable artistic talent. Developed in the mid-nineteenth century, Central Park was the largest and most acclaimed urban park in the country. The park's conception reflected the desire of mostly wealthy landowners and merchants to create a public ground that would rival the ones of London and Paris and establish an international reputation for New York. It was also a solution to the urgent need of city planners to provide a green and tranquil haven for New York's rapidly growing population. William Cullen Bryant in 1844 recommended the establishment of an urban green space, but it wasn't until 1853 that this idea was approved. The eight hundred acre expanse of uneven swampy terrain, bluffs and rocky outcroppings between Fifth and Eighth Avenues spanning from 59th Street to 106th Street (later to 110th Street) was chosen as the site for the park. In 1857 a contest was held to design the park (the first of its kind in the country) and Frederick Law Olmsted and Calvert Vaux submitted the winning entry with their "Greensward Plan." The "Greensward Plan," which challenged the greatest European parks at the time, melded pastoral, picturesque and formal landscape elements influenced by the English romantic tradition. Olmsted's premise for the park's development at once embraced the objectives of the city planners and acknowledged the plights of the urban dweller: "The primary purpose of the Park is to provide the best practical means of healthful recreation for the inhabitants of the city, of all classes. It should present an aspect of spaciousness and tranquility with variety and intricacy of arrangement, thereby affording the most agreeable contrast to the confinement, bustle, and monotonous street-division of the city." (C.E. Beveridge and D. Schulyer, ed., Frederick Law Olmsted, "Creating Central Park, 1857-1861," vol. 3, *The Papers of Frederick Law Olmsted*, Baltimore, Maryland, 1983, p. 212-213)

The park's construction was one of the most extensive public works projects undertaken by New York City during the nineteenth century. In order to create the "natural" landscape designed by Olmsted and Vaux, extensive changes were required of the raw terrain. Over twenty thousand workers were employed to demolish numerous shanty towns and small villages containing churches and schools. The workers blasted out ridges dating back to the Ice Age, using gunpowder in excess of the amount employed at Gettysburg. They also moved over ten million cartloads of soil and transported half a million cubic yards of topsoil to the site to enrich the poor glacier earth. This allowed the planting of over four million trees representing 632 species, and 815 varieties of plants, vines and flowers. Incorporated into Olmsted's and Vaux's plan were various picturesque buildings, bridges, lakes, artificial ponds and fountains. In order to better control traffic of all kinds, the park design mapped out distinct and separate curvilinear carriage routes, pedestrian walks and equestrian paths.

Opened to the public in the winter of 1859, Central Park was used by over seven million people and quickly became a frequent topic of numerous articles, guide books, prints and photographs. Writers by the end of the nineteenth century hailed Central Park as one of the most important and beautiful assets of the country: "You may never have ridden down Potter's Row in London, nor along Champs Elysees in Paris, nor about the Corso in Rome: you may never have gone along the broad gay walks under the Rows

(fig.a) J.S. Johnston, Central Park, The Mall looking north (1894)
© Collection of The New-York Historical Society

of Linden in Berlin, nor roamed throughout the Prater in Vienna, nor listened to the music in the Stadt Garten at Buda Pesth; but if you have gone to Central Park here in New York on a bright morning of spring, summer or autumn you have missed nothing by not seeing those other places. For not in Hyde Park, the Thiergarten, the Prater nor in any of the show places of other capitals could have found more to delight you and make you glad that you are alive that you find here in the green stretches of meadow, the fresh foliage of the trees, the gay bloom of flowers and the clear notes of birds that make Central Park so pleasant a spot in the busy city." (fig. a) (A. Wakeley, "The Playground of the Metropolis," *Munsey's Magazine* 13, September 1895, p. 565.)

Hassam's *Central Park* depicts the often visited Conservatory Water, a manicured pond situated just off Fifth Avenue near Seventy-second Street (figs. b and c). Conservatory Water is a formal Neo-Renaissance concrete basin that was named for a conservatory that was planned to be built in this location, but was never erected. The artificial lake was used as a miniature model boat pond, an activity that was enjoyed primarily on weekends. Hassam in *Central Park* situates the viewer along the east side of the pond looking across to the northwest shore. The painting documents rambling paths, lush manicured lawns, and in the distance a quaint Victorian style cottage (no longer extant) nestled among towering trees and sprawling bushes.

Hassam's interest in parks dates back to his time in Boston, but more prominently to his short residence in Paris in the late 1880s. Hassam moved to Paris with the intent of "refining his talent in the larger crucible of contemporary art." (D.F. Hoopes, *Childe Hassam*, New York, 1982, p. 13). While in Paris, Hassam studied at the Académie Julian though his experience at the school was neither favorable nor beneficial to his art. Working independently of the Académie, Hassam worked on his own, absorbing various tenets of Impressionism. Hassam consistently rejected the classification of Impressionist as Donaldson F. Hoopes writes: "If the search for the equivalent in paint of the light of nature involved borrowing some of the Impressionists' innovations, then he borrowed, but at no time in his career did Hassam subordinate the emotional content of the represented image to a supremacy of color or technique." (*Childe Hassam*, p. 13) Hassam in a later interview with A.E. Ives explained his own principals of style: "Art, to me, is the interpretation of the impression which nature makes upon the eye and brain. The word impression as applied to art has been used, and in the general acceptance of the term has become perverted. It really means the only truth because it means going straight to nature for inspiration, and not allowing tradition to dictate your brush, or to put it

(fig.b) Central Park, Conservatory Water with a view of Temple Beth-El
© *Collection of The New-York Historical Society*

brown, green or some other colored spectacles between you and nature as it really exists. The true impressionism is realism. So many people do not observe. They take ready-made axioms laid down by others, and walk blindly in a rut without trying to see for themselves." (A.E. Ives, "Talks with Artists: Childe Hassam on Painting Street Scenes," *Art Amateur* 27, October 1892, p. 117) Hassam turned to the streets and boulevards of Paris for inspiration, but ventured to the quieter locales of the city's parks for new subjects to paint. There he observed amidst the quiet and manicured lush landscape finely dressed Parisians strolling along the promenades. Works such as *Parc Monceaux* (Private Collection, *circa* 1888–89) illustrate Hassam's earlier interest in the subject of parks and his unique painting techniques, important elements that would mature in his works executed in the following decade in New York.

(fig. c) Central Park, Conservatory Water,
© *Collection of The New-York Historical Society*

(fig. d) Detail

Considered one of the most beautiful passages of the park, Conservatory Water and its immediate environs attracted many artists during the 1890s. Conservatory Water provided Hassam the subject matter with which he and his fellow Impressionists found continual fascination: leisurely activities of the refined and aristocratic in a picturesque setting. In the 1890s Central Park was enjoyed by a mixture of social classes who commonly escaped to the lush surroundings on Sundays and holidays. During the work week, however, the park was frequented typically by upper middle-class women and children who were seeking clean air, restful moments and healthful exercise amidst the rolling lawns, winding paths and elegant promenades of the great park (fig. f). Set against the picturesque backdrop of Conservatory Water, Hassam in *Central Park* populates the canvas with groupings of women and children, but focuses on an elegantly clad young well-to-do mother promenading with her finely garbed child and furry family companion (fig. d). Through his ingenious choice of location and selection of subjects, Hassam successfully captures on canvas an idyllic and quiet moment amidst the frantic urban environment of New York.

The scene which Hassam portrays in *Central Park* moves beyond a visual record of the leisurely activities of New York's elite, but through a deft handling of composition, brush stroke, color, light and atmosphere transforms into a serene and tranquil image. Hassam employs a steady yet broken brush stroke that infuses the work with a sense of graceful movement indicative of the gait of fashionably dressed women, or of the serpentine paths on which they follow. This sophisticated handling of paint combined with a jewel-like palette emphasizes Hassam's atmospheric effect of a light-filled day. In *Central Park*, Hassam depicts a moist spring day composed of rich greens, browns, and yellows. From this dominate color scheme emerges the contrasted brilliance of reds, blues and whites as seen in the figures' clothing, the flower in the central young woman's hat and the dress of the child. Hassam bathes the work with subdued sunlight, an element commonly used by Impressionists to diffuse a scene, which gives form and texture to the figures and landscape.

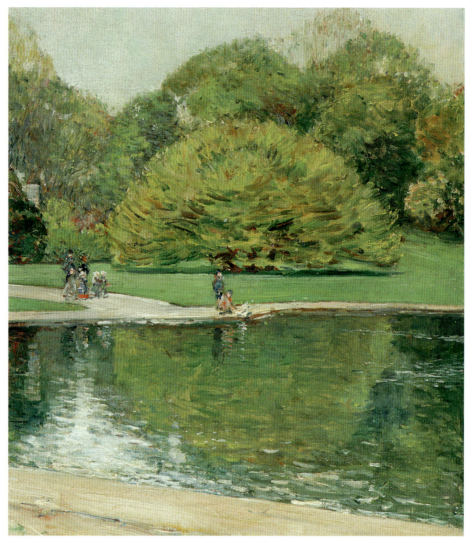

(fig. e) Detail

Hassam's compositional techniques in *Central Park* further underscores the impact of the work and its ability to maintain in a fleeting moment a feeling of calm within a city fraught with consternation and energy. Hassam, though he was committed to nature and an advocate of documenting real life experiences, found that it was necessary to be visually selective in his observations. In an interview in 1892 with A.E. Ives, Hassam explained his compositional methods: "I do not mean to convey the idea that you may at any minute find a subject ready at hand to paint. The artist must know how to compose a picture, and how to use the power of selection. I do not always find the streets interesting, so I wait until I see picturesque groups, and those that compose well in relation to the whole. I always see my picture as a whole. No matter how attractive the group might be, if it was going to drag my composition out of balance, either in line or color, I should resist the temptation of sketching it. I should wait, if it were a street scene, till the vehicles or people disposed themselves in a manner more conducive to a good effect for the whole." ("Talks with Artists: Childe Hassam on Painting Street Scenes," p. 117) Unlike other artists who typically painted Conservatory Water with the prominent and stately buildings of Fifth Avenue in the background, Hassam literally chose to turn his back to these structures and focused on the interior of the park creating a pure urban pastoral. As a result, Hassam afforded himself the opportunity to portray the cultivated landscape of the park without the distractions of looming city structures. The formality of landscape is further emphasized by his balanced composition composed of a series of curvilinear shapes that are punctuated with strategically placed groupings of figures. The dominant curve of the pond is echoed in the various trees and shrubs in the distance and reflected in the placement of the groups of women and children who dot the walking path that meanders into the greenery beyond (fig. e). The building in the distance is the only manmade structure with hard straight edges, but it is cleverly hidden behind verdant branches. As a result Hassam crystallizes the women and children, subtle movements of vegetation, the shimmerings of the pond's reflection and changing sunlight, into an organic symmetry that infuses the work with a sense of timelessness and harmony.

(fig. f) Frank M. Ingalls, Central Park, View of Lady with Two Children (1908)
© Collection of The New-York Historical Society

Through Hassam's Impressionist gaze, the tranquility, serenity and importance of the nation's greatest public park is poignantly recorded in Hassam's *Central Park*. Central Park was, and remains today, a haven that affords inhabitants of New York an escape from the turmoil and oppression of the city. Hassam pays homage to the park's central mission in *Central Park* and creates an iconic image that embraces urbanism in its most beautiful and picturesque form.

This painting will be included in Stuart P. Feld's and Kathleen M. Burnside's forthcoming *catalogue raisonné* of the artist's work.

Estimate on Request

16

VARIOUS PROPERTIES

•16

OTIS KAYE (1885-1974)
Send $ Quick!
signed 'Otis Kaye' (center right)—signed again and inscribed
with various notations on the reverse
oil on canvas laid down on board
16¾ x 23¾ in. (42.5 x 60.3 cm.)

PROVENANCE:
The artist.
By descent in the family to the present owner.

Estimate: $70,000-90,000

17

•17

OTIS KAYE (1885-1974)
Dollars and Cents and the Hundred Guilder Print
signed 'O. Kaye' (lower right)
gouache and pencil over etching
14⅛ x 17½ in. (35.9 x 44.4 cm.)

PROVENANCE:
The artist.
By descent in the family to the present owner.

Estimate: $15,000-25,000

18

•18

LOUIS CHARLES MOELLER (1855-1930)

A Notty Question

signed 'Louis Moeller NA' (lower right)

oil on canvas

10 x 14 in. (25.4 x 35.6 cm.)

PROVENANCE:
William Foster Hooper, Fall River, Massachusetts.
Gift from the above to the present owner.

EXHIBITED:
Fall River, Massachusetts, Fall River Public Library, *Loan Exhibition of Paintings*, March 1899, no. 48
Fall River, Massachusetts, Fall River Public Library, *Art Exhibition*, June 1911, no. 102, as *Discussion*

Estimate: $15,000-25,000

19

VARIOUS PROPERTIES

•19

WILLIAM HOLBROOK BEARD (1823-1900)

Pre-Adamite

signed and dated 'W.H. Beard. 1874' (lower left)

oil on canvas

18 x 24 in. (45.7 x 61 cm.)

PROVENANCE:
A Connecticut family.

Estimate: $30,000–40,000

20

•20

WALTER GAY (1856-1937)
French Interior
signed 'Walter Gay' (lower left)
oil on canvas
18¼ x 22½ in. (46.2 x 57.2 cm.)

PROVENANCE:
Graham Gallery, New York.

Estimate: $20,000-30,000

21

PROPERTY OF A PRIVATE COLLECTOR

•21

THOMAS MORAN (1837-1926)
Venice
signed and dated 'T.Moran. 1897.' (lower right)
watercolor on paperboard
14 x 10in. (35.6 x 25.4cm.)

Estimate: $20,000–30,000

•22

MARY CASSATT (1844-1926)

Ellen with Bows in Her Hair, Looking Right

signed 'Mary Cassatt' (lower right)
pastel on paperboard
22 x 17½ in. (55.9. x 43.8 cm.)

PROVENANCE:
Durand-Ruel, New York.
Little Gallery in the Woods, Kansas City, Missouri.
Mr. and Mrs. Albert L. Reeves, Jr., Hillsborough, California,
acquired from the above *circa* 1920.
By descent in the family to the present owner.

EXHIBITED:
Kansas City, Missouri, William Rockhill Nelson Gallery of
Art—Atkins Museum of Fine Arts, *Homage to Effie Seachrest*,
August-October, 1966

LITERATURE:
A.D. Breeskin, *Mary Cassatt: A Catalogue Raisonné of the Oils,
Pastels, Watercolors, and Drawings*, Washington, DC, 1970, p. 135,
no. 304, illustrated

Ellen with Bows in Her Hair, Looking Right, a portrait of the artist's
niece Ellen Mary Cassatt, is a delightful example of Mary Cassatt's
work in pastel. With remarkably few strokes, Cassatt has managed
not only to depict Ellen Mary, but to evoke the happy innocence
of childhood. Ellen Mary was the second daughter of Mary
Cassatt's brother Joseph Gardner Cassatt. This portrait was
probably executed in 1899 during the artist's only extended visit to
the United States after she had settled in Paris in 1874. By the late
1890s, Cassatt took to pastel as another means of expanding her
artistic realm after having achieved incredible success with her oils
in the Impressionist style. By building up her subject with
countless carefully placed pastel lines and marks, Cassatt created "a
masterpiece of simplicity." (N.M. Mathews, *Mary Cassatt*, New
York, 1987, p. 72)

Indeed images of children are often more powerful than those of
their adult counterparts, for their youth represents vast potential
rather than past accomplishments or acts. At roughly the same time
that Cassatt executed this pastel of her niece, Camille Mauclaire
published this reiteration of the virtues of childhood: "A child is
moving forward, and this is its special beauty, reckless, radiant,
irresistibly affecting, made to bring tears to older eyes. Its
imprudence is disarming and enchanting. A laughing, singing,
lisping, unselfconscious, naked child is extraordinarily, magnetically
attractive." (C. Mauclaire, "A Painter of Childhood" in *L'Art
Decoratif*, August 1902, as quoted in N.M. Mathews, Ed., *Cassatt:
A Retrospective*, New York, 1996, p. 268)

This pastel will be included in the Cassatt Committee's revision of
Adelyn Dohme Breeskin's *catalogue raisonné* of the works of Mary
Cassatt.

Estimate: $350,000-450,000

22

•23

WINSLOW HOMER (1836-1910)

Two Girls and a Boat, Tynemouth, England

signed and dated 'Winslow Homer 1881' (lower left)
watercolor on paper
13⅝ x 19¾ in. (34.6 x 52 cm.)

PROVENANCE:
Charles S. Homer, Jr., New York, by bequest, 1910.
Mrs. Charles S. Homer, Jr., by bequest, 1917.
Urling Valentine Coxe (Mrs. Campbell R. Coxe), Norwalk,
Connecticut, by gift, after 1930.
M. Knoedler & Co., New York, 1936.
William Macbeth, Inc., New York, 1936.
Francis Minot Weld, New York, 1936.
Julia Tiffany Weld (Mrs. Francis Minot Weld), New York, by
bequest, 1949.
M. Knoedler & Co., New York, 1950.
Private Collection, Dallas, Texas, 1950.
By descent in the family to the present owner.

EXHIBITED:
New York, The Metropolitan Museum of Art, *Loan Exhibition of
Paintings by Winslow Homer*, February-March 1911, no. 28
Pittsburgh, Pennsylvania, Carnegie Institute, *Water Colors by
Winslow Homer*, September-October 1923, no. 37
New York, The Museum of Modern Art, *Sixth Loan Exhibition:
Winslow Homer, Albert P. Ryder, Thomas Eakins*, May 1930, no. 25
New York, Wildenstein & Co., *A Loan Exhibition of Winslow
Homer for the Benefit of the New York Botanical Garden*, February-
March 1947, no. 56

The magnificent series of watercolors that Winslow Homer
executed during his twenty month stay in Cullercoats, England is
recognized as some of the artist's finest work. Between the
summer of 1881 and the fall of 1882, Homer immersed himself in
the daily life of that small town located on the northeast coast of
England. Working almost exclusively in watercolor, Homer
recorded the habits and routines of the townspeople, but more
than anything else, he turned to the women of the area for his
subjects. It was largely the fisherwomen, whose robust physical
presence concisely represented the strong will of the town and
impressed the American artist to produce some of the most
poignant and compelling watercolors of his career.

Two Girls and a Boat, Tynemouth, England presents a group of
fisherwomen standing in front of the stern of a fishing boat. Each
woman bears a load: one has a wicker basket, the other a young
child. Their dress is bright and the beach is sunny. While this work
appears at first to be a straightforward description of the activities
that Homer witnessed, it also provides insight into his technical
development as well as into the role that the fisherwomen played
in the English coastal town.

Winslow Homer was immediately impressed by the forceful
demeanor of the fisherwomen. Indeed, "No one could spend any
time in the village without becoming aware of the special qualities
of the fishermen and women. Ruggedly independent, they needed
both endurance and courage, for they had to bear with and battle
the elements for sustenance.... Like most everyone else who visited
Cullercoats, Homer was drawn to the fisherwomen. 'Fair
complexioned, sun-tanned, ruddy cheeks, with strong-built but
supple forms,' they were famous for their beauty. They were, as
one writer put it, 'the great feature of the place.'" (H. Cooper,
Winslow Homer Watercolors, Washington, DC, 1986, p. 116) The
average woman in Tynemouth had an impressively active daily
routine. "Not only did the complete care of the family fall to
them, but its prosperity was largely dependent on their ability to
sell the fish the men caught. As the men slept, the fisherwomen

worked throughout the day. They searched for bait, dug for sand
worms, or gathered mussels, limpets, and dogcrabs from the rocks.
They assisted in the baiting of hooks, helped to push the boats
into the often icy waters at sunset, and pulled them in again at five
or six in the morning when they returned laden with fish. The
fisherwoman was described as healthy and powerful; her ways,
modest and restrained." (*Winslow Homer Watercolors*, p. 117)
Homer not only depicts the pretty faces of the young
fisherwomen, but he makes overt references to their noble duties
by including the large wicker basket (or creel) from which
fisherwomen sold the catch, and the child sleeping peacefully in its
mother's care. The bright dress of the women, while picturesque,
delineates the women's solid vertical forms.

While Homer's watercolors from the late 1870s exhibit blockier
forms and a broad handling of the medium, his Cullercoats
pictures demonstrate a movement toward more refined and
carefully articulated shapes. In general "he rejected minute detail,
excessive control, and tight handling—techniques contrary to the
natural properties of the medium, although used by many highly
praised contemporary watercolorists." (*Winslow Homer Watercolors*,
pp. 111-112) *Two Girls and a Boat, Tynemouth, England* reveals his
continuing development at this early point in his stay in
Cullercoats, yet Homer successfully combines aspects of both
techniques. Like his earlier watercolors, the beach and sky are
depicted with broad and gentle sweeps of watercolor, and he
suggests another figural group by a block of gray wash in the left
of the work. Meanwhile the figural group in the foreground is
rendered in a more delicate manner, with great attention to detail.
The buoyant spirit of the work—from the presence of the young
child to the bright sun, is also characteristic of his early Cullercoats
watercolors, before the intensity of a seacoast winter affected him.

Apart from the deft manipulation of watercolor, the Cullercoats
pictures were embraced because they were noble portraits of
hardworking simple people. They received favorable reviews from
the very beginning. "Despite Homer's reputation as a bold and
unconventional artist, the Cullercoats watercolors surprised the
picture-viewing public. Although well within a traditional
European mode, to most Americans these fisherfolk scenes were
unique. The critic Mariana Griswold Van Rensselaer wrote: 'The
most complete and beautiful things he has yet produced, [and]
among the most interesting American art has yet created. They
are, to begin with, pictures in the truest sense, and not mere
studies or sketches, like most of his earlier aquarelles... The dignity
of these landscapes and the statuesque impressiveness and sturdy
vigor of these figures, translated by the strong sincerity of his
brush, prove an originality of mood, a vigor of conception, and a
sort of stern poetry of feeling to which he had never reached
before.'" (*Winslow Homer Watercolors*, p. 119)

Distinct as a group, yet characteristic of Homer's great facility
with watercolor, all of his Cullercoats watercolors are exceptional
in their universal appeal. Once he returned to the United States,
Homer used oil more often as a medium that he did in England.
However, it was not because he was unsuccessful with watercolor.
In fact, an 1883 show of his work in watercolor prompted a
reviewer from the *Boston Evening Transcript* to write the following
passage: "Homer is both the historian and poet of the sea-coast
life... The whole gamut of watercolor power, from the richness of
elemental life depth and vividness to the density of storm darkness
and human woe, and thence again to life light, joyousness,
delicacy and subtle glow, is here run with a strength and accuracy
that few not seeing will believe it capable of. Indeed it seems to
proclaim its capacity to be perhaps the most artistic of all mediums
when adequately handled." (*Winslow Homer Watercolors*, p. 119)

This painting will be included in the forthcoming Spanierman
Gallery/CUNY/Goodrich/Whitney *catalogue raisonné* of the
works of Winslow Homer.

Estimate: $800,000-1,200,000

23

24

PROPERTY OF A PRIVATE COLLECTOR

•24

JOHN SINGER SARGENT (1856-1925)
Portrait of the Hon. Claire Stuart Wortley
signed 'John S. Sargent' (lower left) and dated '1923' (lower right)
charcoal on paper
24½ x 19 in. (62.2 x 48.2 cm.)

EXHIBITED:
London, England, Royal Academy, *Exhibition of Works by the late John Singer Sargent, R.A.*, January-March 1926, no. 455

This exquisite charcoal drawing exemplifies the bravura technique for which Sargent is so celebrated. According to a note from the sitter's family, the portrait was drawn at Sargent's studio in Tite Street, Chelsea, on Friday July 27, 1923, in one sitting which lasted from 10:30 a.m. until 1:00 p.m.

Estimate: $15,000-25,000

25

PROPERTY OF A PRIVATE COLLECTOR

•25

JOHN SINGER SARGENT (1856-1925)

Bedroom

watercolor and pencil on paper

11⅜ x 9 in. (28.8 x 22.8 cm.)

PROVENANCE:
Violet Sargent.
Mrs. Hugo Pitman (*neé* Reine Ormond), niece of the artist.
David Daniels, New York.

EXHIBITED:
Minneapolis, Minnesota, The Minneapolis Institute of Arts,
Drawings and Watercolors from Minnesota Private Collections, no. 30,
May-June 1971
New York, Whitney Museum of American Art, *John Singer
Sargent*, October 1986-January 1987

John Singer Sargent painted *Bedroom circa* 1880-82, a period of
great innovation in his artistic development. While developing his
skills in the studio of Carolus-Duran from 1874-78, Sargent
temporarily abandoned the medium of watercolor. However, after
1878 and throughout the early 1880s, Sargent rediscovered the
medium, finding in it expressive qualities that suited his emerging
artistic persona. *Bedroom*, most likely painted on a trip to Venice,
exemplifies Sargent's renewed delight in watercolor painting.
Sargent has employed the medium to create an evocative mood.
He has enchanced the simplicity and sparseness of the room with
delicate washes on the broad, empty foreground. Annette
Blaugrund writes, ". . . these watercolors share with each other,
and with Sargent's oils, the conceit of an empty foreground, the
interior scene presents the diagonal recession into the picture
space common to the nineteenth-century French paintings of
Monet, Manet, and particularly of Degas and Caillebotte, which
Sargent probably saw on exhibition in Paris." (*John Singer Sargent*,
New York, 1986, p. 214)

Estimate: $30,000-50,000

•26

WINSLOW HOMER (1836-1910)

The Coral Divers

signed and dated 'Winslow Homer 1885' (lower right)
watercolor and pencil on paper
13 x 20¾ in. (33 x 52.7 cm.)

PROVENANCE:
Edward W. Hooper, Boston, Massachusetts, probably 1886.
Fanny Hooper Curtis (Mrs. Greely S. Curtis), Boston,
Massachusetts, daughter of the above, by 1901.
Estate of Fanny Hooper Curtis, 1963.
Hirschl & Adler Galleries, Inc., New York, 1964.
Acquired by the present owner from the above.

EXHIBITED:
Boston, Massachusetts, Museum of Fine Arts, *Loan Exhibition of
Paintings by Winslow Homer*, February-March 1911, as *Diver,
Nassau*
Boston, Massachusetts, Copley Society, *Paintings in Water Color by
Winslow Homer, John Singer Sargent and Dodge MacKnight*, March
1921, no. 40, as *The Diver*
Paris, France, Association Franco-Américaine d'Expositions de
Peinture et de Sculpture, *Exposition d'Art Américain: John S. Sargent,
R.A., Dodge MacKnight, Winslow Homer, Paul Manship*, May-June
1923, no. 22
Boston, Massachusetts, Museum of Fine Arts, *Watercolors by
Winslow Homer*, Summer 1924
Cambridge, Massachusetts, Fogg Art Museum, Harvard
University, *Water Colors by Winslow Homer, 1836-1910*, May-June
1932, no. 1
Boston, Massachusetts, Museum of Fine Arts, *Exhibition of Works
by Winslow Homer and John La Farge*, June-August 1936
New England Museums Association, *Winslow Homer: Water Colors,
Prints and Drawings*, 1936-37 (This exhibition traveled to Andover,
Massachusetts, Addison Gallery of American Art, Phillips
Academy, September-October 1936; Hanover, New Hampshire,
Dartmouth College, October-November 1936; Northampton,
Massachusetts, Smith College, January-February 1937), p. 17,
illustrated, as *Coral Divers, Bahamas*
Boston, Massachusetts, Friends of the Boston Symphony
Orchestra, *Exhibition of Paintings by Winslow Homer*, December
1937
Miami, Florida, The Lowe Art Museum, University of Miami,
American Painting of the 18th, 19th and 20th Centuries, August 1972
Washington, DC, National Gallery of Art, *Winslow Homer
Watercolors*, March-May 1986, no. 128, pp. 139-140, illustrated
(This exhibition also traveled to: Fort Worth, Texas, Amon Carter
Musuem, June-July 1986; New Haven, Connecticut, Yale
University Art Gallery, September-November 1986)
Miami, Florida, Center for the Fine Arts, *Winslow Homer: Water
and Light, Selected Watercolors 1874-1897*, November 1991-
February 1992
Washington, DC, National Gallery of Art, *Winslow Homer*,
October 1995-January 1996, (This exhibition also traveled to
Boston, Massachusetts, Museum of Fine Arts, February-May 1996;
New York, Metropolitan Museum of Art, June-September 1996),
no. 150, illustrated

"You will see, in the future I will live by my watercolors," said
Winslow Homer prophetically to a friend, and indeed since then
the artist's watercolors have been ranked among the greatest and
most enduring achievements in American art. Helen Cooper
writes, "Executed over a period of more than thirty years, between
1873 and 1905, these works are unsurpassed for their direct
statement, luminosity, and economy of means. . . In oil, Homer's
touch was powerful, exploiting the weight and density of the
medium. In watercolor, it was exquisite, full of sensuous nuance.
The liquid pigment called forth in him a private and poetic vision
that otherwise found no place in his art. Suffused with a special
awareness of the beauty of nature, the fluid, audacious brushwork
and saturated color of the mature works in particular have had a
wide and liberating influence on much subsequent American
watercolor painting." (*Winslow Homer Watercolors*, Washington,
DC, 1986, p. 16)

Winslow Homer executed *The Coral Divers* in the winter of 1885
on his first trip to the Caribbean. A masterwork of control and
expression in watercolor, the composition's luminous color,
vibrant fluid washes and boldness rank it among Homer's finest
achievements in the medium. Helen Cooper writes, "Formally,
the Caribbean light had a liberating—and lasting—effect on
Homer's watercolor style. The Bahamas sheets are painted with
free and gestural strokes in transparent washes often of brilliant
colors, leaving large areas of white paper exposed. Their style was
undoubtedly suggested by the conditions of their creation: painted
outdoors, and quickly, before the watery pigment could dry under
the hot sun. With fewer spongings, scrapings, and lift-outs, they
have a direct, seemingly unpremeditated execution. Homer was
able suddenly to say things with ease that had before been
communicated only with effort." (*Winslow Homer Watercolors*, p.
134)

Homer set sail for the city of Nassau in the Bahamas in December
1884. Nassau was becoming a popular tourist location, and
Century Magazine, for whom Homer had worked in the past,
commissioned the artist to illustrate an article on the city.
Traveling with his father, Homer stayed at the elegant Royal
Victoria Hotel, the largest building on the island whose graceful
veranda commanded a breathtaking view of the city and distant
sea. In this relaxed and inspired setting, Homer created some of
his most luminous and memorable watercolors, among them *The
Coral Divers*, which was executed in January or February of 1885.

Helen Cooper writes, "Sponge diving and coral and conch fishing
also became pictorial subjects. *The Sponge Diver* (Museum of Fine
Arts Boston) is dated 1889, but as there is no evidence he visited
the Bahamas that year, it was probably begun in 1885, its broader,
more fluid washes reflecting Homer's increased facility in the
intervening four years. This sheet and *The Coral Divers* represent a
bronzelike figure bearing his trophy as he emerges lustrous from
the waves. Homer gives these scenes vivid clarity by juxtaposing
colors: the stretch of brilliant blue water shot with pale pink
reflections from the submerged reefs, the white boat achieved
through reserving the paper, and the dusky color of the figures."
(*Winslow Homer Watercolors*, p. 139)

When Homer first exhibited his Caribbean watercolors in New
York and Boston in 1885-86, they were met with great praise,
and critics sensed a new direction in Homer's art. Franklin Kelly
writes, "Still, if the critics were quick to note that Homer's first
tropical watercolors lacked the sense of gravity and seriousness that
so memorably distinguished his Cullercoats sheets, they were
equally quick to notice that in them he had demonstrated an
impressive new handling of the medium. Homer had now found
'color and sunshine' and a 'newborn power of rendering them,' a
frankness and yet a harmony.' And surely the source of that new
power play in the fact that Homer painted these watercolors not
as part of a larger systematic process intended to result in a finished
work of high ambition, but as records of actual experience. They
were, in other words, transcriptions of the visual encounters with
new things in a new land that energized Homer's creative
instincts, 'memoranda of travel,' but also memoranda of
excitement, interest, and pleasure." (*Winslow Homer*, Washington,
DC, 1995, p. 187)

This watercolor will be included in the forthcoming Spanierman
Gallery/CUNY/Goodrich/Whitney *catalogue raisonné* of the
works of Winslow Homer.

Estimate: $1,800,000-2,400,000

26

•27

JOHN SINGER SARGENT (1856-1925)

Constellation: Rainy Day on the Yacht

signed and dated 'John S. Sargent 1924' (lower right)
watercolor and pencil on paper laid down on board
13¼ x 21 in. (33.6 x 53.3 cm.)

PROVENANCE:
Mrs. Nathaniel Bowditch Potter (née Mary Sargent), gift from the
artist.

By descent in the family to the present owner.

Executed in 1924 while John Singer Sargent was visiting with
family and friends near Cape Cod Massachusetts, *Constellation:
Rainy Day on the Yacht* is a brilliant expression of form, color and
light. Sargent has taken the subject of two women sitting on the
afterdeck of a yacht—in this case his cousins Mary and Henrietta
Sargent—and created a virtuoso watercolor, exploiting the
medium's luminosity and vivid color.

The importance of watercolor in Sargent's career has long been
acknowledged. Annette Blaugrund writes, "In the twentieth
century, watercolor began to play a more dominant role in
Sargent's oeuvre. The marked rise in his production has often been
explained as a release from the burden of portraiture and as a
private endeavor indulged in during vacations. Some even have
said that his sister Emily's interest in watercolor led to his
predilection for the medium. More important, as Hardie observed,
was the fact that in watercolor he found endless scope for his
driving need of 'unhampered personal expression.' Watercolors of
this period no longer are preparatory studies linked to oil paintings
nor slight works to be distributed as gifts. By the early 1900s, the
watercolor medium, familiar to him from childhood, best suited
his artistic needs as well as his way of life." (*John Singer Sargent*,
New York, 1986, p. 219)

Throughout his career Sargent traveled frequently, and later in his
career his watercolor case and sketching pads were nearly always
with him. During his travels after 1900 however, he particularly
enjoyed the companionship of close friends and extended family.
Constellation: Rainy Day on the Yacht reflects the genteel company
in which Sargent felt most at ease: the artist has painted his two
cousins during an excursion on a rainy day aboard the yacht
Constellation. (fig. a) This spectacular vessel belonged to Herbert
Sears, another prominent Bostonian and avid yachtsman.

Sargent's close relationship with his two Boston cousins is well
documented. The woman seated at left is Mrs. Nathaniel
Bowditch Potter, *neé* Mary Sargent. To the right is Mary Sargent's
sister Henrietta Sargent Lowell. Henrietta's husband was the
architect Guy Lowell who designed the Museum of Fine Arts,
Boston, where Sargent painted his great cycle of murals beginning
in 1916. Both women were daughters of Charles Sprague Sargent,
the renowned Harvard botanist, who among other achievements,
created the Arnold Arboretum in Brookline, Massachusetts. The
artist was a frequent guest at 'Holm Lea,' Charles Sprague Sargent's
home in Brookline, while visiting the Boston area.

Sargent was particularly close to his cousin Mary Sargent. His
correspondence from these years is filled with cordial words of
news from friends in common or interesting bits of observations
about their travels. Sargent often kept Mary updated about the
progress of his murals for the Museum of Fine Arts. As the artist's
cousin and sister-in-law of the museum's architect, Mary Sargent
Potter had particularly close connections to this great project
undertaken at the end of the artist's career.

In *Constellation: Rainy Day on the Yacht* Sargent has depicted a
relaxing and informal moment aboard the yacht. His two cousins
smile as they sit on deck, wrapped in shawls or blankets against the
damp air. A tarpaulin has been draped overhead and lends the
scene a vivid, diffuse light. Details in the watercolor, such as the
yacht's rigging reflected on the watery deck, are executed in
Sargent's most fluid and virtuoso style—the hallmarks of his finest
work in the medium.

This work will be inlcuded in the forthcoming John Singer
Sargent *catalogue raisonné* by Richard Ormond and Elaine
Kilmurray, in collaboration with Warren Adelson and Elizabeth
Oustinoff.

Estimate: $300,000-400,000

(fig. a) Photograph of the yacht 'Constellation' owned by Herbert Sears, circa 1825.

27

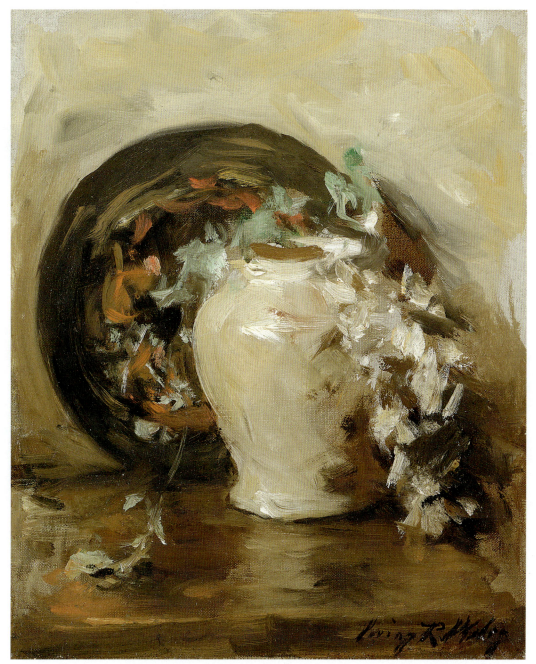

28

VARIOUS PROPERTIES

•28

IRVING RAMSEY WILES (1861-1948)
·Still Life with Vase and Plate
signed 'Irving R Wiles' (lower right)
oil on canvas
13¼ x 11¼ in. (33.7 x 28.6 cm.)

PROVENANCE:
Chapellier Galleries, Inc., New York.

EXHIBITED:
St. Joseph, Missouri, Albrecht Gallery—Museum of Art, *The Art of Irving Ramsey Wiles*, April-May 1971, no. 14, illustrated

Estimate: $20,000-30,000

29

•29

CHARLES COURTNEY CURRAN (1861–1942)

Golden Glow

oil on canvas

30 x 20 in. (76.2 x 50.8 cm.)

Estimate: $30,000–50,000

•30

FREDERICK CARL FRIESEKE (1874-1939)

Yellow Tulips

signed 'F.C. Frieseke' (lower right)

oil on canvas

31¾ x 31¾ in. (80.1 x 80.1 cm.)

EXHIBITED:

Detroit, Michigan, Detroit Museum of Art, *Paintings by Frederick C. Frieseke, Gardner Symons, and James R. Hopkins*, October 1917 (This exhibition also traveled to Milwaukee, Wisconsin; Minneapolis, Minnesota; Pittsburgh, Pennsylvania, The Carnegie Institute of Arts, 1918)

Pennsylvania Academy of the Fine Arts, *116th Annual Exhibition*, February-March 1921, no. 430, as *Yellow Tulips: The Mirror*

LITERATURE:

Emporium, vol. 38, no. 277, November 1913, p. 337, as *Tulipani Gialli*

P. Trenton and W.H. Gerdts, *California Light 1900-1930*, Laguna Beach, California, 1990, pp. 42, 44, as *Reflections* (or *The Birdcage*), illustrated

Executed at the height of his career, *Yellow Tulips* exemplifies Frederick Carl Frieseke's goals of creating a perfectly balanced and pleasing composition. Frieseke's home in Giverny, the setting for a number of his finest pictures, is depicted here with dazzling color and vitality. The sunlight that shines through the windows provides an opportunity to show the play of light and shadow with consummate Impressionist technique. In this work Frieseke has chosen one of his favorite conventions, a female subject clothed in an elegant fabric. Her placement in the composition is novel, however, and perhaps unique in the artist's work: the model, his wife Sadie, is painted as a reflection in a mirror. Below the mirror, arranged on a mantlepiece, are porcelain objects of virtu—and the yellow tulips which lend the painting its name.

Frieseke's interest in sunlight began in Giverny, and remained with him throughout his career. Indeed, one of the principle subjects of *Yellow Tulips* is the light which pervades every corner of the composition. In a 1914 interview he elaborates on this hallmark of his art, which amounts to an adoration of the sensuous possibilities of sunlight: "It is sunshine, flowers in sunshine, girls in sunshine, the nude in sunshine, which I have principally been interested in for eight years and if I could only reproduce it exactly as I see I would be satisfied." (E. B. Neff, *American Painters in the Age of Impressionism*, Houston, Texas, 1994, p. 119) Expanding on the theme of flower painting in particular, he adds that "my idea is to reproduce flowers in sunlight...to produce the effect of vibration, completing as I go... If you are looking at a mass of flowers in the sunlight out of doors you see a sparkle of spots of different colors; then paint them in that way... One should never forget that seeing and producing an effect of nature is not a matter of intellect but of feeling... The effect of impressionism in general has been to open the eyes of the public to see not only sun and light, but the realization that there are new truths in nature." (C.T. MacChesney, "Frieseke Tells Some of the Secrets of His Art," *New York Times*, June 7, 1914)

The figure's dress, the chairs, windows and hanging fabrics all provide further opportunities to add pattern to the composition. William H. Gerdts has noted that "it was Frieseke who introduced into the repertory of Giverny painting the concern for rich, decorative patterns, related to the art of Edouard Vuillard, Pierre Bonnard, and the other Nabi painters. There are patterns of furniture, patterns of parasols, patterns of fabric and wall coverings, patterns of light and shade, and patterns of flowers, all played off one another in bright sunshine...." (*Monet's Giverny: An Impressionist Colony,* New York, 1993, p. 172) All of Frieseke's artistic devices come together in this work to form a highly successful, complete, composed and balanced composition.

Frieseke first settled in Giverny following a summer spent there in 1900. Among the Americans who established themselves in Giverny, Frieseke lived and worked in the town the longest, remaining for nearly two decades. By 1906, the artist had moved into the former house of the American painter, Theodore Robinson, who lived next to Claude Monet. The intricate and extravagant garden of the French Impressionist painter had a significant impact on Frieseke, and Frieseke's home also had a "beautiful old garden, running riot with flowers." (*Monet's Giverny: An Impressionist Colony, p. 172*) This blending of an American Impressionist style with typically French subjects resulted in Frieseke's prominence at home and abroad; the March 1932 issue of *Art Digest* called him "the most internationally renowned American artist."

Painted about 1911-12, *Yellow Tulips* exemplifies the best of Frieseke's early work. It was during the years between 1906 and 1919 that Frieseke painted some of his most remarkable canvases. As B. L. Summerford wrote in an essay on the artist, "there is a thrilling quality to the early paintings. They have the vitality of youth, the feeling that anything is possible...In many ways they are among his finest and freest conceptions, direct, forceful, confident and economical." (*A Retrospective Exhibition of the Work of F. C. Frieseke,* San Francisco, California, 1982, p. 17) Because of its importance, Frieseke exhibited *Yellow Tulips* twice, first in 1917 and 1918 at museums in Detroit, Milwaukee, Minneapolis and Pittsburgh, and secondly in 1921 at the Pennsylvania Academy of the Fine Arts under the title *Yellow Tulips—The Mirror*. A major rediscovery, *Yellow Tulips* is a signature example of the artist's finest impressionist masterworks.

This painting will be included in the forthcoming catalogue raisonné of Frieseke's work being compiled by Nicholas Kilmer, the artist's grandson.

Estimate: $800,000-1,200,000

30

31

VARIOUS PROPERTIES

•31
WILLIAM CHADWICK (1879-1962)
Early Sping Flowers
signed 'W. Chadwick' (lower left)
oil on canvas
30 x 30¼ in. (76.2 x 77.8 cm.)

PROVENANCE:
By descent in the family to the present owner.

Estimate: $25,000-35,000

32

•32

EDWARD HENRY POTTHAST (1857-1927)

Bathers

oil on canvas laid down on masonite
20 x 27¾ in. (50.8 x 70.4 cm.)

Estimate: $40,000–60,000

•33

RICHARD EDWARD MILLER (1875-1943)

The Garden at Giverny

signed 'Miller' (lower right)
oil on canvas
23½ x 28½ in. (59.2 x 72.4 cm.)

Celebrated for his paintings of women in interiors and out-of-doors, Richard E. Miller depicts in this composition a corner of a garden. The subject of the painting is a simple arrangement of two wicker chairs and a folding table, upon which a white table cloth is laid for a light repast. Over the scene hangs a Japanese lantern which is consistent with Miller's delight in Asian motifs, for his paintings often include oriental porcelains, parasols, silks or fans.

Of his palette, the overall effect is of dazzling sunlight. Robert Ball describes Miller's distinctive technique: "The brilliance of unmixed color fascinated Richard; it began to invade all his painting and consume his thought. Color was broken up, and ingenuity invented ways to create the illusion of light. The subject became something to play the light upon, with all its vibration, diffraction, reflection. For Richard, light was a sort of bombardment from the sun. The problem: how to capture it. And he did, breaking the colors against everything in wild harmonies. Black, the absence of color, was not in harmony. Rejected also were the handsome earth colors. Burnt sienna was retained to mix with blue for making any required dark, but there was little mixing. The colors in their own crudity set up their own state and became harmonious when placed together in his bold, instinctive way. He was a discerning and forceful painter. His canvases strongly project themselves, his colors are vibrant and clear..." (R. Ball and W. Gottschalk, *Richard E. Miller, N.A., An Impression and Appreciation,* St. Louis, Missouri, 1968, n.p.)

In *The Garden in Giverny,* the outward subject of this sun-dappled composition is a table set for a simple meal, perhaps just for one person, as a single coffee cup rests on the table cloth. In relation to his prolific, figural work, Miller creates an expectation where his usual model, a young woman, has seemingly stepped away, or is about to return. The artist thus suggests a subtle thematic tension in a painting otherwise emblematic of only a quiet moment in the corner of a garden.

Estimate: $180,000-220,000

34 No Lot

33

VARIOUS PROPERTIES

•35

EDWARD CUCUEL (1875-1951)
The Reflection
signed 'Cucuel' (lower right)—signed again on the stretcher
oil on canvas
35¼ x 43¼ in. (89.5 x 109.8 cm.)

PROVENANCE:
Private Collection, West Germany

Estimate: $80,000-120,000

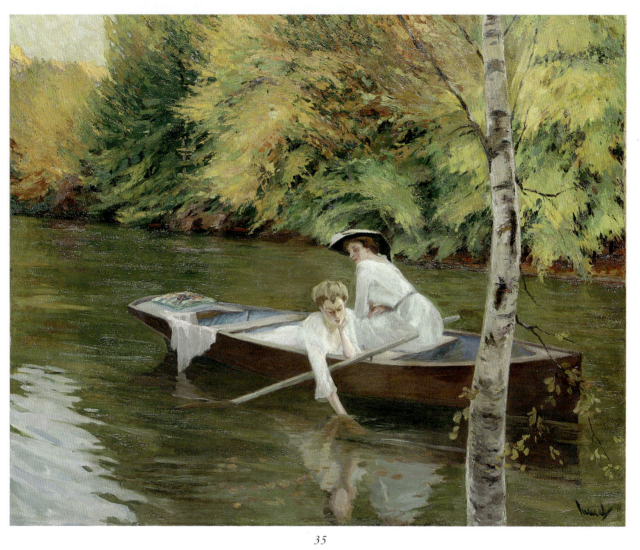

35

•36

WILLIAM JAMES GLACKENS (1870-1938)

Vacation Home

signed and dated 'W. Glackens 11' (lower right)—signed again and inscribed indistinctly on the reverse
Oil on canvas
26 x 32 in. (66 x 81.3 cm.)

PROVENANCE:
Estate of the artist.
Ira Glackens, son of the artist.
Kraushaar Galleries, New York.
Grete Meilman Fine Art, Ltd., New York.

LITERATURE:
R.J. Wattenmaker, "William Glackens's Beach Scenes at Bellport," in *Smithsonian Studies in American Art*, vol. 2, no. 2, Spring 1988, pp. 78-9, illustrated

Summer leisure time, a predominant theme in the work of many American Impressionists, captivated William Glackens throughout the 1910s. He began depicting seaside resorts as early as 1908 in Cape Cod, but his most impressive works of this type were painted in Bellport, Long Island. From the summers of 1911 through 1916, Glackens and his family spent the summer in this small coastal community on the southern shore of Long Island. The series of paintings that he executed during these summers are among his finest as he imaginatively explored new painting techniques and developed his own style of Impressionism.

Throughout his career, Glackens was drawn to active settings where he could derive inspiration from the bustle of the characters that inhabited each place. While residing in New York City during the majority of the year, he produced a number of paintings of Washington Square and Central Park in the early 1910s. He was drawn to the animated motion in both parks: in the Washington Square series, he focused on the rituals in the park, from the people on the buses to the parades that took place there. In the Central Park works, he vigorously described the winter sports that the park had to offer. However, by 1911, Glackens turned to beach scenes, a more conventionally Impressionistic subject matter. In much the same manner as his parks series depicts New Yorkers "hurrying about their business, traveling on foot, by automobile, by electric tram, or by double-deck bus." (W.H. Gerdts, *William Glackens*, New York, 1996, p. 102), his Bellport pictures depict a multitude of people enjoying all of the pleasures that are offered by the rustic seaside community.

Bellport, Long Island was an ideal place for an artist to experiment artistically as it had a great deal to offer for imagery, and it was a place where Glackens could work unencumbered by outside pressures. "Glackens's son Ira recalls that at the time 'Bellport was a simple place, cottages, nothing showy. Bellport was still an unspoiled town, and life was largely confined to the village street. There were no large estates in the neighborhood. Near the beach stood a huge barnlike 'Vacation Home' for New York shopgirls which supplied subjects for many of my father's canvases. A ferry every fine day took bathers across the bay to the ocean beach, Old Inlet, whose rolling white dunes and scraggly bayberries and beach plums saw many picnics.'" (R.J. Wattenmaker, "William Glackens's Beach Scenes at Bellport," in *Smithsonian Studies in American Art*, vol. 2, no. 2, Spring 1988, pp. 77-9)

In *Vacation Home*, Glackens has taken full advantage of all that a summer day in Bellport had to offer. In the foreground, he presents a large group of figures in the water, either bathing alone, or frolicking in small groups. Further into the composition is the bright sandy beach, with vibrant green grass and a number of figures moving in various directions. The lush green trees sway in the summer wind, and Glackens has managed to include the stately architecture of the Vacation Home as well as an American flag, unfurled and flapping in the wind. Naturally drawn to the activities on the beach, Glackens uses them to foster his artistic development by experimenting with new brushstrokes and intensity of color. Richard Wattenmaker writes of *Vacation Home*: "The canvas is characterized by impressionistic tonality, color contrasts, and brushwork. To these are added Glackens's very personal feeling for rugged, sparkling juicy color and for emphatic contrasts of colors and shapes. The chunky, cut-glass surface of the blue water, the crisp terseness of the figures, the patterns of the trees and buildings, the smoother consistency of the clouds and sky, all create a multiplicity of shapes with contrasting textural quality. Demarcations are clear and clean-cut; the foreground figures are played off against the angled, faceted shapes of the open gazebo on the left, the dressing sheds on the right, and the walls and roofs beyond. All are gleaming, infused with sunlight. Space is circumscribed by the forceful stepladder layering of patterns, with notes of surprising boldness, such as the striking green band beneath and beyond the trees to the right rear of the gazebo, as well as the diminutive figure in the blue skirt on the steps in the distance, all of which reveals Glackens's imaginative presentation of his visual world." (R.J. Wattenmaker, "William Glackens's Beach Scenes at Bellport," pp. 77-9)

The pictures that William Glackens painted in Bellport, Long Island with their bold color schemes and representations of form and space, represent the artist's vivid imagination at its best. It is therefore no wonder that they were "not only the pictures he most frequently exhibited but also his most popular, judging by their presence today in many of America's leading art institutions. They also enjoyed the most critical attention in their own time and were addressed again in the most serious scholarly study that Glackens has received in recent years." (W.H. Gerdts, *William Glackens*, p. 109) Apart from their astounding aesthetic appeal, their popularity derives from their modern treatment of a conventionally appealing subject matter. While a number of his fellow American artists focused on the same type of subject, Glackens's beach scenes have a quality that make them unique. "One reviewer perhaps best summed up the character of his beach and park pictures: 'His world is a restless reflection of himself—a world crowded with a multitude of accidents and incidents all worth recording; all crying out to be recorded and all unseen by most of us, for most of us have grown a hard shell around our curiosity." (*William Glackens*, p. 113)

Estimate: $900,000-1,200,000

36

37

•37

THEODORE EARL BUTLER (1861-1936)

Fireworks, Vernon Bridge

signed 'TE Butler' (lower left)—signed 'Theodore E. Butler' dated '1908' and inscribed with title on the reverse before lining

oil on canvas

21¼ x 25¾ in. (54 x 65.4 cm.)

PROVENANCE:
Estate of the artist.
James Butler, son of the artist.
Spanierman Galleries, Inc., New York.
Maxwell Galleries, San Francisco, California.
Sotheby's, New York, May 28, 1987, lot 186.
Acquired by the present owner from the above.

EXHIBITED:
San Francisco, California, Maxwell Galleries, *Theodore Earl Butler*, June-July 1972, no. 676, illustrated

This work will be included in Patrick Bertrand's forthcoming *catalogue raisonné* of the work of Theodore Earl Butler.

Estimate: $40,000-60,000

38

•38

GIFFORD BEAL (1879-1956)

Lawn Party, Old Salem

signed 'Gifford Beal' (lower left)—signed again and
inscribed 'Old Salem' on the reverse

oil on panel

24 x 36 in. (61 x 91.5 cm.)

Estimate: $80,000-120,000

•39

CHILDE HASSAM (1859-1935)

Alkalis, Rabbit and Grease Wood Squaw, Oregon Trail

signed and dated 'Childe Hassam 1908' (lower left)—inscribed with artist's monogram and dated again on the reverse before lining, and inscribed with title on a piece of the original stretcher attached to the backing

oil on canvas

20 x 30¼ in. (50.8 x 76.8 cm.)

PROVENANCE:

American Academy of Arts and Letters, New York.

Milch Gallery, New York.

ACA Gallery, New York.

Dr. Milton Luria, Verona, New Jersey.

Irma Rudin, New York.

RELATED WORKS:

Afternoon Sky, Harney Desert, oil on canvas, 20⅛ x 30⅛ in. (51.1 x 76.5 cm.), Portland Art Museum, Portland, Oregan

In the fall of 1908, Childe Hassam traveled to Oregon for the second time in his career to visit his friend, Colonel Charles E. S. Wood, a resident of Portland and a noted patron of the arts. Four years before, Hassam had traveled west to install a mural in Wood's home. On this second visit, Hassam apparently set out almost immediately for the desert country which had enthralled him before. Writing a postcard home, Hassam noted that he'd traveled with Wood two hundred miles into the desert, finding "trout a thousand miles long. Mallard ducks so thick they knock the hat off when you put your head out of cover. Venison hoe cakes and alfalfa honey. Here is some on the card. [signed] Marco Polo Muley Hassam." "Muley" was a nickname conferred on Hassam by his artist friends. (W. Hiesinger, *Childe Hassam, American Impressionist,* New York, 1994 p. 136)

Hassam produced a great many oils of the desert, more than thirty in all, including his celebrated *Golden Afternoon* (Metropolitan Museum of Art, New York). In 1909, Hassam presented a group of East Oregon pictures at Montross Gallery in New York, followed by a second exhibition of his desert paintings in Portland.

A closely related oil, *Afternoon Sky, Harney Desert* (Portland Museum of Art, Portland, Oregon), exhibits a similar interest in capturing the vastness of the desert landscape. In both paintings, Hassam employs a low horizon to emphasize the deep recession of space. He renders the desert grasses with pale browns and ochres, as if bleached by the sun, and the sky with whites and pale blues. In painting the light and dry desert air of the Harney region, the artist delighted in the solitude of the place: "I was at a point," he wrote, "the furthest removed from railroad and telegraph in the United States...the Harney desert is probably the least accessible place on this continent. The nearest town—Ontario, Ore.—is 187 miles distant. The desert is on a plateau forty five hundred feet above sea level. The air is limpid and liquid, the skies are stupendous and the distances amethystine:" (Burke, *American Paintings in the Metropolitan Museum of Art, Volume III* New York, 1980, p. 359)

This painting will be included in Stuart P. Feld's and Kathleen M. Burnside's forthcoming *catalogue raisonné* of the artist's work.

Estimate: $150,000-250,000

39

40

PROPERTY OF A PRIVATE COLLECTOR

•40

JOHN SINGER SARGENT (1856-1925)

Study for the Boston Museum Murals; and Study for the Boston Public Library Murals:
Two Works

the first: charcoal on paper laid down on paper; the second: charcoal on paper
the first: 25 x 19 in. (63.5 x 48.2 cm.); the second: 18¾ x 24½ in. (47.6 x 62.2 cm.)   (2)

PROVENANCE:
The first:
Bernard Black, New York.
David Daniels, New York.
The second:
Miss Emily Sargent and Miss Violet Ormond.

In 1916 John Singer Sargent was commissioned to decorate the rotunda of the Museum of Fine Arts, Boston—a project that would become the focus of his professional efforts for the rest of his life. To complete the murals of *Classic and Romantic Art* and *Apollo and Daphne* Sargent made extensive figural studies. Among his favorite models at the time was Thomas McKeller, the figure in the present work.

In 1895 and again in 1903 Sargent travelled to Boston to oversee the installation of his murals at the Boston Public Library, a commission that he had initially received in 1890. The present drawing relates to the figure of Moloch in the murals.

These two figural drawings exemplify Sargent's virtuoso draftsmanship—they are imaginative, uninhibited, and graphically intense. His affinity for the beauty of line and the male figure finds expression in the works, with their rich modeling and careful observation of light cast over the human form.

Estimate: $20,000-30,000

41

•41

JOHN SINGER SARGENT (1856-1925)

Persian Artifact with Faience Decoration

watercolor and pencil on paper

13 x 9⅝ in. (33 x 24.4 cm.)

PROVENANCE:
Mrs. Hugo Pitman (*neé* Reine Ormond), niece of the artist.
Gertrude Stein, Paris, France.
David Daniels, New York.

EXHIBITED:
New York, Whitney Museum of American Art, *18th & 19th American Paintings From Private Collections*, June-September 1972, no. 66

John Singer Sargent was always attracted to the beautiful and the exotic. Over the course of his career he created works of art that highlighted the inherent beauty of his subject matter. *Persian Artifact with Faience Decoration* reflects the artist's affinity for an exquisitely decorated ancient vase that he encountered during his extensive travels along the Mediterranean coast. In this watercolor Sargent has taken great care to highlight the subtle beauty of the object—carefully modulated washes are layered so as to suggest the passage of time on the piece of pottery. A soft, evocative light falls from left to right, highlighting the object and suggesting a mysterious, other worldly quality.

Estimate: $50,000-70,000

•42

CHILDE HASSAM (1859-1935)

Naples

signed, dated and inscribed with title 'Childe Hassam Naples 1897' (lower right)—signed with artist's monogram, dated and inscribed with title again on the panel stretcher
oil on canvas
25⅜ x 30⅞ in. (64.4 x 78.5 cm.)

PROVENANCE:
American Academy of Arts and Letters. New York, bequest from the artist, 1930.
The Milch Galleries, New York.
Governor and Mrs. Herbert H. Lehman, New York.
By descent in the family to the present owner.

EXHIBITED:
New York, The Lotos Club, *Eighty-fifth Anniversary Exhibition*, March-April 1955, no. 11
Amherst, Massachusetts, Mead Arts Building, Amherst College, *The 1913 Armory Show in Retrospect*, February-March 1958, no. 21
Washington, DC, The Corcoran Gallery of Art, *Childe Hassam: A Retrospective Exhibition*, April-August 1965, no. 25 (This exhibition also traveled to Boston, Massachusetts, Museum of Fine Arts, August-September 1965; Manchester, New Hampshire, The Currier Gallery of Art, September-October 1965; New York, The Gallery of Modern Art, November-December 1965)
New York, Whitney Museum of American Art, *18th and 19th Century American Paintings in Private Collections*, June-September 1972, no. 33
Williamstown, Massachusetts, Sterling and Francine Clark Art Institute and Williams College Museum of Art, *Paintings from the Collection of Governor and Mrs. Herbert H. Lehman*, 1986, no. 18

In December 1896, Hassam and his wife sailed for a year-long visit to Europe, arriving in Naples, Italy. He remained there to paint through January of the following year before departing for other places on the continent and in England. While abroad, Hassam continued to explore the pictorial possibilities of high vantage points, painting sweeping panoramic landscapes of a kind he had previously begun in New York. Increasingly his style also undertook a shift towards an emphasis in abstract patterning, shown here in the highly-developed painterly qualities of *Naples*. "In fact," writes Ulrich Hiesinger, "Hassam came to prefer motifs in nature that inherently favored such patterns of surface, as he consciously strove to narrow the gap between representation and decoration." (W. Hiesinger, *Childe Hassam, American Impressionist,* New York, 1994, p. 109) In *Naples,* Hassam employs a succession of quick, patterned strokes of the brush, creating a tapestry-like effect of color, enlivened with Mediterranean hues of reds, pinks, yellows, and blues, and a sense of dazzling light.

By tradition, this painting has been recorded as one of six oils exhibited by the artist in the famed Armory Show of 1913, where he included an oil entitled *Naples* and likewise dated 1897. Accordingly, this work was also included in the 1958 exhibition at the Mead Art Museum, in Amherst, Massachusetts: *The 1913 Armory Show in Retrospect.*

This painting will be included in Stuart P. Feld's and Kathleen M. Burnside's forthcoming *catalogue raisonné* of the artist's work.

Estimate: $250,000-350,000

42

43

•43

FRANCIS COATES JONES (1857-1932)
Nymphs in the Autumn Woods
signed 'Francis C. Jones' (lower left)
oil on canvas
36 x 30 in. (91.5 x 76.2 cm.)

Estimate: $15,000-25,000

44

•44

JULIUS LEBLANC STEWART (1855-1919)
Sunlight
signed 'JLStewart' (upper left)
oil on canvas
51½ x 45½ in. (129.5 x 115.5 cm.)

Estimate: $60,000-80,000

45

•45

LOUIS CHARLES MOELLER (1855–1930)

The Connoisseurs

signed 'Louis Moeller N.A.' (lower right)

oil on canvas

18 x 24 in. (45.8 x 61 cm.)

Estimate: $15,000–25,000

46

•46

JOHN GEORGE BROWN (1831-1913)

Eating the Profits

signed and dated 'J. G. Brown, N.A., N.Y. 1878' (lower right)

oil on canvas

21 x 17in. (53.4 x 43.2cm.)

Estimate: $20,000–30,000

•47

WILLIAM MICHAEL HARNETT (1848-1892)

After the Hunt

signed, dated and inscribed 'WMHarnett 1885. Paris' (lower left)

oil on canvas

18 x 10½ in. (45.7 x 26.6 cm.)

In 1885 William Harnett moved to Paris from Munich to test his artistic abilities at the Salon des Beaux Arts. Before his departure, he had completed three of the four renditions of *After the Hunt*, his brilliant *trompe l'oeil* still lifes depicting arrangements of game and hunting gear, hanging dramatically against a dark wooden door with elaborate metal hinges. Once he settled in Paris, he began work on the fourth and final version of *After the Hunt* (The Fine Arts Museums of San Francisco, Mildred Anna Williams Collection), "his greatest virtuoso effort." (E.J. Connell, "After the Hunt," in *William Michael Harnett*, Fort Worth, Texas, 1992, p. 277)

Of the four versions of *After the Hunt*, the last has proved to be the most dynamic. Larger and more complex than the other three, the implicit motion of the picture is so strong that it can be described as a dance routine: "The picture is highly charged with animation, humor and wonder. The dead animals are whimsically choreographed: a partridge executes a perfect upside-down pirouette at center stage, within the circumference of the hunting horn, while below, its mate imitates the stance in mirror image. The hare, still the bloodied, clinical specimen of the *Trophy of the Hunt*, is now positioned with its foot poised as if to spin the hunting horn like a wheel of fortune." ("After the Hunt," p. 277)

In the present work, Harnett combines the deadpan realism of his *trompe l'oeil* technique with a poetic gracefulness. The refined curve of the bird's body extends throughout its entire body to the tip of its feet. Its head is upheld in the most haughty manner, ironically by the string that binds it to the nail in the door. Its arrogant manner effectively rejects the viewer's inquisitive gaze. The razor sharp highlight on the bird's extended wing is not only an exhibition of the artist's talent, but helps transcend the work beyond a clinical study by immediately grabbing the viewer's attention. Virtually identical to the bird that hangs to the right of the ill-fated hare in the final version of *After the Hunt* (The Fine Arts Museums of San Francisco, Mildred Anna Williams Collection), is the single game bird in this work, upon which Harnett has chosen to concentrate all of his efforts. By highlighting a single game piece, the artist returns to his practice of several years earlier, just as he began the *After the Hunt* series. A small group of Harnett's Munich works of the early 1880s depicts a single bird against a wooden door that successfully incorporates the witty irony of Harnett's entire body of work. His inert game birds challenge the viewer either by returning the intense scrutiny or by exhibiting startlingly human posture.

This type of hanging still life is precisely what Harnett's late nineteenth century patrons were seeking. However, *After the Hunt* and its related works count for only one section in a long line of *trompe l'oeil* still lifes by the artist. Catering to his patrons' taste for both antiques and recognizable elements of their daily lives, Harnett depicted game pieces, antique bric-a-brac, newspapers, mugs and pipes. The majority of Harnett's works are comprised of just these elements. What can be discerned about Harnett's patrons is that they were wealthy—whether they inherited their wealth or earned it. Some were "sophisticated men who supported the founding and growth of the museums and art institutions" (D. Bolger, "The Patrons of the Artist," in *William Michael Harnett*, Fort Worth, Texas, 1992, p. 74), while others "began as store clerks, bookkeepers and salesmen [who] worked hard to achieve the affluence they enjoyed." ("The Patrons of the Artist," p. 74) Both groups would have been keenly interested in works that reflected their personalities. Some of his patrons would identify most strongly with the books, pipes and mugs that were parts of their daily lives, while others would have been drawn more strongly to the connotations behind one of Harnett's hunting pictures, where "instead of being an accurate record of a particular event, Harnett's paintings evoke more a broadly conceived aura of the hunt. Wealthy gentlemen, his intended patrons, would recognize and admire these references to the success of their sporting exploits." ("After the Hunt," p. 277)

Harnett's hanging still lifes would have been the ultimate recognizable and fashionable work of art in the late nineteenth century. In fact, "hanging still lifes first became popular in the 1850s through prints by Currier and Ives after game pieces by Arthur Fitzwilliam Tait. In the mid-1870s, L. Prang and Company published a series of 'Dining-Room Pictures' that included game pieces of waterfowl hanging in front of a neutral background. These chromolithographs, reproduced from paintings by George N. Cass and G. Bossett, were destined to decorate many a Victorian dining room and parlor." ("After the Hunt," p. 281)

Harnett holds an exceptional spot within the context of late nineteenth century still life painting, due in equal parts to his virtuoso technique and to his subtle wit. In few instances are these two attributes so magnificently displayed than in this version of *After the Hunt*. It leaves no question as to why Harnett's series "became a prototype for many successive hanging game and other vertical still lifes." ("After the Hunt," p. 285)

Estimate: $600,000-800,000

47

48

VARIOUS PROPERTIES

•48

Thomas Moran (1837-1926)

Crossing the Brook Near Plainfield, New Jersey

signed and dated 'TMoran -78' (lower left)—signed and
dated again and inscribed with title on the reverse

oil on canvas

20 x 30 in. (50.8 x 76.2 cm.)

PROVENANCE:

R.U. Leonori, Jr., and Co., St. Louis, Missouri.

This painting will be included in Stephen L. Good's and Phyllis
Braff's forthcoming *catalogue raisonné* of the artist's work.

Estimate: $40,000-60,000

49

•49

FRANCIS AUGUSTUS SILVA (1835–1886)
Twilight Along the River
signed and dated 'F.A. Silva 79' (lower right)
oil on canvas
24 x 20in. (61 x 50.8cm.)

Estimate: $40,000–60,000

50

•50

JOHN FREDERICK KENSETT (1816-1872)

The Front Range, Colorado

oil on canvas

9¾ x 13¾in. (24.7 x 34.9cm.)

PROVENANCE:
Sale: New York, Association Hall, *The Collection of Five Hundred paintings and Studies by the late John F. Kensett*, March 24-29, 1873.

Estimate: $20,000–30,000

The Lost "Green-horn"

51

•51

ALFRED JACOB MILLER★ (1810-1874)

The Lost "Green-horn"

signed with artist's monogram (lower left)—inscribed with title (upper right)

pencil, ink, inkwash and gouache on paper

8½ x 11½ in. (21.6 x 29.2 cm.)

PROVENANCE:
The artist, Baltimore, Maryland.
Laurence Vernon Miller, Baltimore, Maryland, brother of the artist, by gift from the above, 1839.
Credilla Miller, Baltimore, Maryland, wife of the above.
Credilla Miller Wickham, daughter of the above.
Credilla Wickham Bordley, by decent from the above.
By descent in the family.

Estimate: $60,000-80,000

52

•52

EANGER IRVING COUSE (1866–1936)
Klickitat Brave
signed 'E. I. Couse' (lower right)
oil on canvas
12¼ x 9¼in. (31 x 23.5cm.)

PROVENANCE:
Kennedy Galleries, Inc., New York.

LITERATURE:
Kennedy Quarterly, vol. V., no. 1, October 1964, p. 51, illustrated

This painting will be included in Virginia Couse Leavitt's forthcoming *catalogue raisonné* of the artist's work.

Estimate: $15,000–25,000

53

•53

JOSEPH HENRY SHARP (1859-1953)
Eagle Hunter—Hondo Cañon
signed 'JHSharp' (lower left)
oil on canvas
20 x 16 in. (50.8 x 40.6 cm.)

PROVENANCE:
Newhouse Galleries, Inc., New York.

Estimate: $40,000–60,000

•54

THOMAS MORAN (1837-1926)

Glen Eyrie, Garden of the Gods, Colorado

signed and dated 'TMoran. N.A. 1901.' (lower right)

oil on canvas

36 x 50 in. (91.5 x 127 cm.)

PROVENANCE:
William A. Bell, London, England and Manitou, Colorado, acquired directly from the artist *circa* 1901.
By descent in the family to the present owner.

EXHIBITED:
New York, The Century Club, March 1901.

LITERATURE:
N. K. Anderson, *Thomas Moran*, Washington, DC, 1997, p. 266.

Thomas Moran painted *Glen Eyrie, Garden of the Gods, Colorado* in 1901, a period in the artist's career when he enjoyed preeminence as America's foremost painter of the West. Moran's grand vision of light, space and the majesty of the natural world has come to define the Western landscape in the American imagination.

Glen Eyrie, Garden of the Gods, Colorado depicts the extraordinary natural formations near Manitou Springs, the most fashionable resort in Colorado during the late nineteenth century. Joni Louise Kinsey writes, "The earliest and most important of these [resort towns] was the complex of Colorado Springs and Manitou, at the base of Pikes Peak and near the famed Garden of the Gods...the picturesque site of a series of mineral springs, and on its incorporation in 1870, when the Denver & Rio Grande Railway reached nearby Colorado Springs, it became one of Colorado's most important resorts of the late nineteenth century. Called the 'Saratoga of the West,' it catered to a wealthy clientele of health seekers who came to obtain the famed cure of the mineral waters...the combination of dry rarefied air, the springs' variety of temperatures and chemical contents, and Manitou's special amenities made it the resort of choice for well-to-do consumptives." (*Thomas Moran and the Surveying of the American West*, Washington, DC, 1992, p. 155)

Moran has focused the composition of *Glen Eyrie, Garden of the Gods, Colorado* on the majestic geological formation of the Garden of the Gods. Light falls across the towering form, emphasizing its heroic size and scale. Massive geological formations such as these had powerful symbolic meaning for the artist and nineteenth-century viewers. "Biblical names were given to pinnacle formations throughout the West, reflecting the missions of many early settlers, such as the Mormons, and also the impression the sites conveyed. Most of the features in Zion [National Park] are so christened, as are a number of those clustered in the Garden of the Gods, near Colorado Springs. Towers embodied cosmic significance for a variety of viewers, a fact Moran's art powerfully expressed." (J. Kinsey, *Thomas Moran and the Surveying of the American West*, p. 35)

Although the area around the Garden of the Gods was in the midst of commercial development as a major tourist and resort destination, Moran has painted the landscape in *Glen Eyrie, Garden of the Gods, Colorado* in a pristine, natural state. The geological formations do not bear the mark of human progress; instead, the composition evokes the passage of natural history and the timeless beauty of the natural world. While the central tower in the middleground imparts a great vertical thrust to the composition, Moran has painted the sky and clouds to suggest deep, open space into the far horizon. The breadth and scale of *Glen Eyrie, Garden of the Gods, Colorado* further emphasize the vastness of the landscape of the American West.

Glen Eyrie, Garden of the Gods, Colorado has a particularly distinguished history of ownership, having been acquired directly from the artist by Dr. William A. Bell. Bell was a wealthy British physician and capitalist who purchased in 1880 Moran's great composition of 1875 *The Mountain of the Holy Cross*(Autry Museum of Western Heritage, Los Angeles, California) to hang in Briarhurst, his Manitou, Colorado home. Bell had visited the American West as early as 1867 and signed on with the Kansas Pacific Railroad Survey as a photographer. His survey experiences gave him a broad view of the American West and an appreciation for the value of visual imagery, and they presented him with a new career that was to have significant impact on the West's development. "Bell, already a man of influence in England, was intrigued with the underdeveloped West's commercial possibilities, and formed an early alliance. . . to found. . . what was then to be the single most important corporation in Colorado's early history, the Denver and Rio Grande Railway. Like other lines . . . the Denver and Rio Grande Railway was built on an elaborate structure of financing, construction, and promotional enterprises, a number of which had significant connections to Moran's art and the U.S. geological surveys."(J. Kinsey, p.154)

As a masterwork in Moran's mature style, *Glen Eyrie, Garden of the Gods, Colorado* embodies the confluence of art and business that marked the early development of Colorado Springs and the area around Manitou. The painting's pristine vision of a vast, unspoiled wilderness underscores Moran's commitment and devotion to the majesty and splendor of the American West.

This painting will be included in Stephen L. Good's and Phyllis Braff's forthcoming *catalogue raisonné* of the artist's work.

Estimate: $600,000-800,000

54

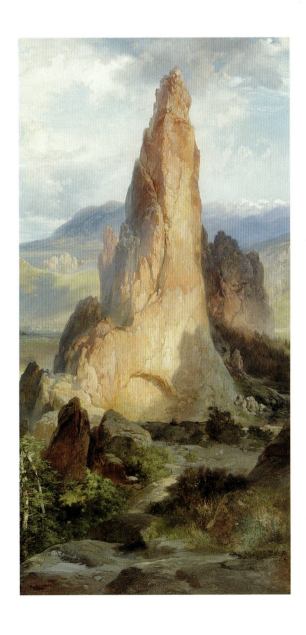

55

VARIOUS PROPERTIES

•55

FREDERIC REMINGTON (1861–1909)
The Fight in the Cañon
signed 'Remington' (lower right), inscribed indistincly with
title and 'The Aztec Treasure House' (lower center)
gouache and ink on paper
18½ x 21⅜ in. (47 X 54.3 CM.)

PROVENANCE:
Kennedy Galleries, Inc., New York

LITERATURE:
J. Ralph, "Shoot! Shoot!" in *Harper's Weekly*, January 11, 1890, p.
28, illustrated
P.H. Hassrick and M.J. Webster, *Frederic Remington: A Catalogue
Raisonné of Paintings, Watercolors and Drawings*, Vol. I, Cody,
Wyoming, 1996, no. 1010, p. 319, illustrated

Estimate: $50,000–70,000

56

VARIOUS PROPERTIES

•56

FREDERIC REMINGTON (1861–1909)

Picking a Way Down

signed 'Frederic Remington' (lower left)
ink, ink wash and gouache on paperboard
25¼ x 18¾ in. (64.2 x 47.7 cm.) (sight size)

LITERATURE:
Harper's Weekly, January 12, 1895, p. 35, illustrated
P.H. Hassrick and M.J. Webster, *Frederic Remington: A Catalogue Raisonné of the Paintings, Watercolors and Drawings*, Vol. II, Cody, Wyoming, 1996, no. 1765, p. 496, illustrated

Estimate: $30,000–50,000

•57

CHARLES MARION RUSSELL (1864-1926)

Outnumbered

signed, dated and inscribed with artist's skull device 'CM Russell 1898' (lower left)
oil on board
11¾ x 17¾ in. (29.8 x 45.1 cm.)

PROVENANCE:
Acquired directly from the artist.
By descent in the family to the present owner.

Charles Marion Russell, known as a cowboy artist, is famous for his dramatic portrayals of life on open the frontiers of Montana. His images, derived directly from experiences he encountered on the open-range, were devoted particularly to the subject of Native Americans and the trials and often dangerous adventures of frontiersman. *Outnumbered* from 1898 is part of series of works that documented the nefarious trappers who populated the open prairie.

Frederick Renner writes: "The welcome that the Indians extended to early explorers and traders eventually wore thin as more and more whites invaded the Indians' land. The first big influx followed the creation of the great fur companies, whose employees and the free trappers who traded with them sought a fortune in beaver and other valuable furs. Even a heavily armed party of these resolute characters found it hazardous to get caught in the dreaded Blackfeet country." (*Charles M. Russell, Paintings, Drawings and Sculpture in the Amon Carter Museum*, Fort Worth, Texas, 1974, p. 136.) Renner further explains: "Free trappers with covetous eyes on beaver in the Blackfeet country employed either of two stratagems for safety. One was to go alone with a trusted companion, travel at night, and try to avoid being seen by the hostile Indians in the daytime. The other was to form a larger party of heavily armed men and depend on sheer numbers and fire power to withstand attack from any wandering party. There was danger in both methods. Even the larger parties usually had to make a run for it if they were caught in open country. If they could reach the timber, where they could fort up and hold off the attack, some of them might live to tell of their experience." (*Charles M. Russell*, p. 157)

By the end of the 19th century, Montana's open frontier was no longer, but Russell, in his works, maintains the much loved vision of The Old West. *Outnumbered*, capturing with great energy and drama a group of traders narrowly escaping the dangers of their attacking foe, offers a rarified glimpse into a memorable history of the Old West.

Estimate: $250,000-350,000

57

58

•58

ALBERT BIERSTADT (1830–1902)
The Sierra Nevadas
signed 'ABierstadt' (lower left)
oil on paper laid down on canvas
19 x 28 in. (48.3 x 71.1 cm.)

Estimate: $50,000–70,000

59

•59

EDGAR S. PAXSON (1852-1919)
The War Party
signed and dated 'E.S. Paxson –2-1901' (lower left)
oil on canvas
39¼ x 27½ in. (99.6 x 69.8 cm.)

PROVENANCE:
Newhouse Galleries, Inc., New York.

Estimate: $60,000–80,000

60

•60

ANNA HYATT HUNTINGTON (1876-1973)

'Yawning Tiger,' A Bronze Figure

inscribed 'Anna V. Hyatt' and stamped 'GORHAM CO. Q 509' and numbered '63'
28 in. (71 cm.) long, rich brown patina

COMPARATIVE LITERATURE:
J. Conner and J. Rosenkranz, *Rediscoveries in American Sculpture: Studio Works 1893-1939*, Austin, Texas 1989, pp. 76, 78, illustration of another example

Also listed in the Groham Foundry records as *Stretching TIger*, the present model of 1917 was edited in bronze in two sizes: the present size and 13¼ inches long. The records indicate that 118 casts of this larger size were made between 1919-1945.

Estimate: $15,000–25,000

•61

NEWELL CONVERS WYETH (1882-1945)

Three Indians in Maine

oil on canvas
39 x 24 in. (99 x 61 cm.)

This work is included in the N.C. Wyeth *catalogue raisonné* database that is being compiled by the Brandywine River Museum and Conservancy, Chadds Ford, Pennsylvania.

Estimate: $100,000–150,000

61

62

•62

ALFRED JACOB MILLER★ (1810-1874)

Pocohontas

signed with artist's monogram (lower left)

oil on paper

8¾ x 8¼ in. (22.2 x 21 cm.)

PROVENANCE:
The artist, Baltimore, Maryland.
Laurence Vernon Miller, Baltimore, Maryland, brother of the
artist, gift from the above, *circa* 1860.
Credilla Miller, Baltimore, Maryland, wife of the above.
Credilla Miller Wickham, daughter of the above.
Credilla Wickham Bordley, by descent from the above.
By descent in the family.

Estimate: $60,000-80,000

63

•63

JOSEPH MOZIER★ (1812-1870)
'Jephthah's Daughter', A Marble Figure
signed, dated and inscribed 'J. Mozier Sc Rome 1864' and
inscribed 'JUDGES.XI.35.36'
65¾ in. (167 cm.) high, on a 26¾ in. (68 cm.) three-part
marble base

LITERATURE:
L. Taft, *The History of American Sculpture*, New York, 1969, p. 109

Estimate: $25,000-35,000

•64

SANFORD ROBINSON GIFFORD★ (1823-1880)

Indian Summer

signed and dated 'S R Gifford 1861' (lower left)
oil on canvas
11 x 19¾ in. (27.9 x 50.2 cm.)

PROVENANCE:
Alexander Gallery, New York.
Acquired by the present owner from the above.

EXHIBITED:
Washington, DC, Adams, Davidson Galleries, Inc., *Masters of the American Landscape*, December 1985-February
1986,

LITERATURE:
I. Weiss, *Sanford Robinson Gifford (1823-1880)*, New York, 1977, p. 199, no. VI H 5, illustrated, as *Indian
Summer in Maine*
I. Weiss, *Poetic Landscape: The Art and Experience of Sanford R. Gifford*, Cranbury, New Jersey, 1987, p. 224,
illustrated

Painted in 1861, *Indian Summer* depicts a wilderness scene of distant peaks glimpsed across a still and mirror-like
lake. Along the thickly forested shore, the artist places a cluster of tepees on a small promontory, along with
several Indians and canoes. The entire landscape is bathed in the rich, atmospheric light for which the artist was
celebrated even in his day.

His friend and fellow artist J. Ferguson Weir wrote in 1880 that "Gifford loved the light. His finest impressions
were those derived from the landscape when the air is charged with an effulgence of irruptive and glowing
light." (J. K. Howat, et al, *American Paradise, The World of the Hudson River School*, New York, 1988, p. 220)
Gifford's contemporary Henry T. Tuckerman called the artist "a noble interpreter of American scenery," and
praised his idealization of the wilderness, and his elevation of landscape painting to a higher, even poetic plane.
"His best pictures, " Tuckerman wrote, "can be not merely seen but contemplated with entire
satisfaction...they do not dazzle, they win; they appeal to our calm and thoughtful appreciation; they minister to
our most gentle and gracious sympathies, to our most tranquil and congenial observation." (*Book of the Artists*,
New York, 1967, p.524-5)

More recent historians have also found the brilliant light in Gifford's art to be the central aspect of his oeuvre,
and the one which unifies his work with the other artists of his time. "Atmosphere," writes one historian,
"—the palpable representation of space, with its sublimated contents, so emphasized by Durand in his 'Letters
on Landscape Painting' as the sign of true mastery of the landscape art—is the indissoluble link that connects the
Luminism of Kensett, Heade, and Gifford with the Hudson River School." (*American Paradise*, p. 47).

With the signal characteristics of Gifford's best luminist landscapes, *Indian Summer* represents a high-point of his
art. It also conveys Gifford's avowed aim of his earliest days, to capture the essential nature of the "forest
primeval," the untouched American wilderness.

Estimate: $250,000-350,000

64

•65

WILLIAM BRADFORD (1823-1892)

Among the Ice Floes

signed and dated 'Wm Bradford 78' (lower right)

oil on canvas

32¼ x 52 in. (81.9 x 132.1 cm.)

PROVENANCE:
Gottfrid Stensakra, Sweden.

Bradford first set out for the northernmost latitudes of the arctic in the summer of 1861, visiting Labrador and Greenland to paint some of the earliest images of this remote region. While there, he also conducted an extensive photographic survey, and recorded his encounters with the indigenous "Esquimaux" people. Nearly every year over the following decade, Bradford mounted additional expeditions to the arctic, using his photographs and numerous sketches to form the basis of his many later compositions in oil. As noted by John Wilmerding, "an immensely successful career followed in the wake of his pursuit of the exotic, so similar to Church's. Bradford got extensive backing for later trips, and was subsequently rewarded with publication of his accounts in England and the sale in 1875 of a painting to Queen Victoria." (J. Wilmerding, *American Marine Painting*, New York, 1987, p. 138)

Taking note of the artist's fidelity to the appearance of ships and topography, the nineteenth-century art-historian Henry Tuckerman quoted at length a contemporary account of one Bradford's arctic excursions: "The vessel encountered its first ice about the middle of the month, in the vicinity of Cape Clear, and from that period to the latter part of August, when it was headed homeward, it was never out of sight of icebergs and icefloes. For two weeks at one time, the vessel was frozen in a field of ice five or six hundred miles in extent, and so surrounded by it that it rose like a wall several feet above the taffrail. It may be readily imagined that sketching out of doors in such a region, even in the middle of summer, with the thermometer in the neighborhood of thirty degrees Fahrenheit, was not a comfortable occupation, however exciting it might have been. Clad in the sealskin suits of the Esquimaux, Mr. Bradford managed to protect himself from the cold sufficiently to enable him to make many studies, some of them very remarkable in color, and all novel and interesting in subject. The larger part of his studies are of icebergs, various in their forms, some resembling grand old castles and ruins, and others of odd fantastic shapes. When the sun falls full upon them their color is a pure dazzling white; but the portions which are in shade are blue, or green, or purple, fading into delicate tints of gray, and shot with rays of pink and saffron." (H.T. Tuckerman, *Book of the Artists*, New York, 1967, pp.554-5)

Among the Ice Flows is one of Bradford's largest masterworks. In it, the artist depicts two icebound ships enveloped in an atmospheric light and a fog gently rising in nearly windless air. Numerous figures busy themselves with the work of the expedition, while in the distance two icebergs tower over the awe-inspiring and rugged landscape. *Among the Ice Flows* is a majestic example of the artist's most striking legacy, his interpretations of the arctic wilderness.

Estimate: $150,000-250,000

65

66

•66

JOHN FREDERICK PETO (1854-1907)

Still Life with Inkwell, Quill and Books

bears spurious signature 'WMHarnett' (lower right)
10½ x 8¼ in. (26.6 x 20.9 cm.)

The relationship between John Frederick Peto and William Michael Harnett has proved to be one of the most fascinating puzzles of twentieth century American art history. In the late 1940s, when Alfred Frankenstein was working on a comprehensive study of American still life, he devised two basic classes of William Michael Harnett's work: those in his "hard" style and those in his "soft" style. His research also coincidentally led him to John Frederick Peto, then a virtually unknown artist.

After considerable research, it dawned on Frankenstein that these paintings in Harnett's "soft" style, were actually the work of John F. Peto such as the present lot. Over time, however, many of these works by Peto had acquired Harnett signatures, presumably signed by individuals hoping to associate their paintings with the then-more celebrated artist. Many paintings by John Frederick Peto have had spurious Harnett signatures subsequently removed. This example however stands as a testament to the development of our understanding of both Harnett's and Peto's oeuvre.

A letter from Alfred Frankenstein accompanies the lot.

Estimate: $30,000-50,000

67

•67

THOMAS HILL★ (1829-1908)

Still Life with Roses and Wine Glasses

signed and dated 'T.Hill 1855' (lower left)

oil on canvas

29 x 36in. (73.7 x 91.5cm.)

Estimate: $50,000–70,000

•68

SEVERIN ROESEN* (1815-*circa* 1872)

Fruit Still Life with Glass of Lemonade

signed and dated 'S. Roesen 1850' (lower right)
oil on canvas
26¼ x 40 in. (66.6 x 101.6 cm.)

PROVENANCE:
Vose Galleries, Boston, Massachusetts.
The Stoufer Corporation.
Armbruster Fine Arts, Chicago, Illinois.

LITERATURE:
J.H. O'Toole, *Severin Roesen*, Cranbury, New Jersey, 1992, p. 129, illustrated

Although relatively little is known about Severin Roesen's life, working habits, formal education and artistic training, he remains one of the most important figures in the history of American nineteenth century still life painting. His lush still lifes of both fruit and flowers are magnificent examples of American taste for representations of the lavish. Dr. William H. Gerdts has noted that "He is certainly the most famous of all mid-nineteenth-century American specialists today, and judging by the great number of enormous pictures painted by him, it seems that he also was tremendously popular in his own time. Furthermore, the many works that have appeared in recent decades, which are at least similar to Roesen's oeuvre, suggest a powerful influence of Roesen upon other artists." (*Painters of the Humble Truth*, Columbia, Missouri, 1981, p. 84)

Roesen's still lifes of fruit and flowers appealed to his nineteenth century patrons due to their lush composition yet logical content. Indeed, the artist "was preoccupied with recreating the opulent splendor of nature which celebrated the pleasures of the physical world in an optimistic manner." (J. O'Toole, *Severin Roesen*, Cranbury, New Jersey, p. 32) He went to great lengths to include a tremendous variety of fruit and flowers in each work. In his best works, "the fruit and flowers are combined in great proliferation, leaving no area unfilled. The fruit, flowers, birds' nests, and man-made decorative objects of ceramic and glass are sometimes piled up on a double-tiered table, the tiers almost always of grained grayish marble, which appears to have been his preference. While these often gigantic paintings of literally hundreds of objects have been interpreted as Victorian *horror vacui*, they are also the ultimate embodiment of mid-century optimism, representing the richness of the land, the profusion of God's bounty in the New World, his blessing upon the American Eden throughout his cornucopia of plenitude." (*Painters of the Humble Truth*, p. 87)

Fruit Still Life with Glass of Lemonade is indeed a *tour de force* of Roesen's talent. In a dark and moody setting, the artist has piled a marble tabletop with the most sumptuous fruit and decorative objects. Roesen has arranged them in a pyramid shape, culminated cleverly by grape vines, whose winding tendrils reach to the top of the composition. Roesen has depicted some of the most uncommon fruit of the nineteenth century including cherries, blackberries, raspberries, red and green grapes, a watermelon, peaches, plums, pears, apricots, and a tiny flower group in the foreground on the left. No doubt intrigued by the water's distortion on objects, Roesen has chosen to depict a spoon emerged in a glass of lemonade.

In the manner of many nineteenth century American artists, Roesen had a number of favored elements that he used time and again in different compositions. Although this artistic practice like might make his work appear repetitive, Roesen was highly capable of "capturing the individual characteristics in his subject matter with a sensation of lushness and immediacy that must have, at one point, come from careful study of nature. For example, the tight, luminescent skin of each grape in a cluster looks full and three-dimensional. This is achieved by subtle juxtapositions of colors that change quickly within each orb from white highlights to brownish centers to shades of green and purple. Likewise, the outer skin of the lemon peel is pebbled and hard; the contours of the yellow-to-red peaches are softly blurred; the fragile petals of the roses are almost translucent and their stems are bristling with sharp, fuzzy thorns." (*Severin Roesen*, p. 35) The carefully conceived compositions and masterful technique that evident in *Fruit Still Life with Glass of Lemonade* are characteristic of Roesen's finest still lifes. These qualities have inspired Dr. William H. Gerdts to classify Roesen within the vast tradition of American still life painting as one of only seven American artists who "stand out as being among the most significant still-life specialists of the mid-century." (*Painters of the Humble Truth*, p. 84)

Estimate: $200,000-300,000

68

69

•69

JOHN FREDERICK KENSETT★ (1818–1872)
New England Composition Scenery
signed 'Kensett' and inscribed with title and '753' on the
stretcher
oil on canvas
10 x 18 in. (25.4 x 45.6 cm.)

Estimate: $25,000–35,000

70

•70

ALBERT BIERSTADT (1830-1902)

A River Estuary

signed 'ABierstadt' (lower right)

oil on paperboard laid down on masonite

12¼ x 18½ in. (31.1 x 47 cm.)

PROVENANCE:
Christie's, New York, December 2, 1977, lot 38.

Estimate: $30,000-50,000

71

•71

GUY WIGGINS (1883-1962)
5th Avenue on Washington's Birthday
signed 'Guy Wiggins' (lower left)—signed again and
inscribed with title on the reverse
oil on canvas
30 x 25 in. (76.2 x 63.5 cm.)

Estimate: $25,000–35,000

72

•72

EDMUND WILLIAM GREACEN (1877-1949)
On the Hudson
signed and dated 'Edmund Greacen 1913-' (lower right)
oil on canvas
26 x 36 in. (66 x 91.5 cm.)

PROVENANCE:
Estate of the artist.
By descent in the family.
Private collection, Atlanta, Georgia.

Estimate: $35,000–45,000

•73

ERNEST LAWSON (1873-1939)

Union Square, New York in Winter

signed 'E. Lawson' (lower left)

oil on canvas

24⅜ x 20 in. (61.9 x 50.8 cm.)

PROVENANCE:
The Milch Galleries, Inc., New York.
Sundel and Margaret Doniger, New York, *circa* 1950.
By descent in the family to the present owner, *circa* 1970.

Ernest Lawson painted *Union Square in Winter* just after the turn of the century, when he and other members of the Eight created their most dramatic images of urban America.

Like his fellow Ashcan painters and many American Impressionists who preceded him, Lawson was fascinated by the modern American city and the lives of the people who inhabited it. In *Union Square in Winter*, the artist has chosen to depict the city at that moment when the frantic urban pace slows after a snowfall. Like Childe Hassam, who at this time was also painting images of New York in the snow (such as *Winter in Union Square*, Metropolitan Museum of Art, New York) Lawson selected a commercial part of the city, a snow-covered square whose open expanse and 19th-century buildings grace the city scape. Just visible through the wintry haze is the rounded cupula of the old German Savings Bank. Near the center of the composition, Lawson depicts Henry Kirke Brown's 1856 equestrian statue of George Washington, a focal point of the square. Numerous pedestrians traverse the streets encircling the monument, including a push-cart vendor, one of the storied fixtures of turn-of-the-century New York.

As an early meditation of street life and the urban landscape, *Union Square in Winter* recalls other Ashcan canvases of New York, such as Robert Henri's masterwork, *Snow in New York*, 1902 (National Gallery of Art, Washington, D.C.). *Union Square in Winter* likewise proclaims its Ash-can heritage with its rich, lustrous impasto and emphasis on city dwellers within the urban milieu. Lawson has developed here a narrow tonal range of whites, blues and greens. Highlights have been added with touches of warmer-toned reds, seen especially in the wares of the vender, and pinks, seen in the brownstone in the distance. This subtle mixture of colors and bold painting technique is the hallmark of Lawson's style.

His immediate inspiration was likely his mentor John H. Twachtman, whose nearly monochromatic depictions of the Connecticut countryside Lawson undoubtedly saw while a student of Twachtman and J. Alden Weir in Cos Cob, Connecticut, in the 1890s. Lawson's innovation with *Union Square in Winter* is to transform the tonal elements of Twachtman's art into an urban setting, softened with snow fall. In this way Lawson would create an entirely new vision of a great metropolis by joining the lyrical qualities of American Impressionism with the avant-garde painting of the Eight.

Estimate: $150,000-250,000

73

•74

MARY CASSATT (1844-1926)

Susan in a Toque Trimmed with Two Roses

oil on canvas

25½ x 21¼ in. (64.8 x 53.9 cm.)

PROVENANCE:

Ambroise Vollard, Paris, France.

Galerie Charpentier, Paris, France, 1-2 April, 1954, no. 62, as *Jeune Femme é La Toque*.

Sotheby's, London, England, 26 June 1990, lot 8.

Acquired by the present owner from the above.

LITERATURE:

A.D. Breeskin, *Mary Cassatt: A Catalogue Raisonné of the Oils, Pastels, Watercolors and Drawings*, Washington, DC, 1970, no. 105, p. 65, illustrated

Mary Cassatt painted *Susan in a Toque with Two Roses* about 1881, not long after her first participation with the French Impressionists, with whom she showed in 1879 at their fourth exhibition. "If we look at the paintings and pastels of the early days of Cassatt's Impressionist affiliation," writes Nancy Matthews, "we can discern her efforts to achieve the new realism touted by the Impressionists...Most striking is Cassatt's interest in capturing life in its normal and unposed state....Although a simple concept, the naturalistic effect in art was hard won, requiring subtle adjustments of form and content and a concentrated effort to achieve the appearance of effortlessness." (*Mary Cassatt*, New York, 1987, p. 43) As Judith Barter recently noted, Cassatt's sources for her art were varied. "To devise compositional strategies for her depictions of women in public and private places, Cassatt looked not only to the traditions of society portraiture but also to illustrations in contemporary fashion magazines. She was not alone in this: her new colleagues, including Paul Cezanne, Claude Monet, and Berthe Morisot, had earlier turned to these sources for thematic and compositional models." (*Mary Cassatt: Modern Woman*, Chicago, 1998, pp.47-8.)

Her subject in the present work is a young woman fashionably dressed for the out-of-doors, in a dark, fur-trimmed coat and stylish hat. Apparently she is seated, as if on a bench, with the trunk of a tree visible over her right shoulder. The painting relates in its subject, a young woman, to many of Cassatt's paintings of this period, perhaps most closely to her painting of 1880 entitled *Autumn* (Musée du Petit Palais, Paris). Both are freely rendered, half-length portraits of a young woman, seemingly lost in thought, her attention fixed elsewhere.

In the case of the present picture, her model, Susan, is the daughter of her housekeeper, Mathilde Vallet, and was a favorite model of the artist in the 1880s. Cassatt paints her as a girl, only a few years beyond childhood into adolescence. In contrast to the background, which is broadly and rapidly painted by Cassatt, lending an effect of plein-air painting, the young woman's face is highly finished. She executes the work with clear pinks and blues, and with brush strokes of rich color, marking this as one of the finest and most pleasing examples of Cassatt's early portraits.

This painting will be included in the Cassatt Committee's revision of Adelyn Dohme Breeskin's *catalogue raisonné* of the works of Mary Cassatt.

Estimate: $800,000-1,200,000

74

PROPERTY FROM
A PRIVATE COLLECTION, NEW YORK

•75

BIRGE HARRISON (1854-1929)

Fifth Avenue in Winter

signed 'Birge Harrison' (lower right)
oil on canvas
30 x 18 in. (76.2 x 45.7 cm.)

PROVENANCE:
Hirschl & Adler Galleries, Inc., New York.

EXHIBITED:
New York, Hirschl & Adler Galleries, Inc., *Picturing Gotham: New York City Through the Eyes of its artists*, January-March 1996

Estimate: $150,000-200,000

75

76

VARIOUS PROPERTIES

•76

JONAS LIE (1880-1940)
Monhegan Island
signed 'Jonas Lie' (lower right)
oil on canvas
30 x 60 in. (76.2 x 152.4 cm.)

PROVENANCE:
A Connecticut family.

Estimate: $20,000-30,000

77

•77

EDWARD CUCUEL (1875-1951)

The Small Boat

signed 'Cucuel' (lower left)—signed again and inscribed
with title on the stretcher

oil on canvas

31½ x 31½ in. (80 x 80 cm.)

Estimate: $50,000-70,000

•78

JANE PETERSON (1876-1965)

On the Pier, Edgartown

signed 'Jane Peterson' (lower right)
oil on canvas
29 x 36¼ in. (73.7 x 92.1 cm.)

PROVENANCE:
Estate of the artist.
Sale: Ipswich, Massachusetts, O. Rundle Gilbert, *Public Auction: Jane Peterson Philipp*, August 9 & 10, 1966.
Clifford D. Hanson, Sandwich, Massachusetts, acquired from the above.

LITERATURE:
J.J. Joseph, *Jane Peterson, An American Artist*, Boston, Massachusetts, 1981, p. 10, illustrated

"Jane Peterson is not an Impressionist", nor, as Patricia Jobe Pierce explains, "is she a Neo- or Post-Impressionist. She is not an Art Nouveau or Nabi painter. She is not a follower of Prendergast. She is not a Fauvist. Incredibly, Jane Peterson does not belong to any single school of painting. Having absorbed technical points and emotional input from many artists, teachers and trends, Peterson developed her own approach to painting." (J.J. Joseph, *Jane Peterson: An American Artist*, 1981, p. 18) Executed in 1916, *On the Pier, Edgartown*, composed of striking color and bold line illustrates the hallmarks of Peterson's unique painting style and represents one of her foremost achievements in oil.

Peterson was born in Elgin, Illinois and began her artistic training in 1896 at Pratt Institute in New York under the instruction of Arthur Wesley Dow. After graduating from Pratt in 1901, Peterson over the next decade held various teaching positions that brought her to Boston and Maryland. During this time she continued her studies at the Art Student's League as well as with the leading European artists of the period such as Frank Brangwyn, Jacques-Emile Blance and Joaquin Sorolla y Bastida in Paris, Venice and Madrid. She also traveled extensively throughout exotic North Africa visiting places such as Biskra, Egypt and Algiers. Drawing inspiration from her travels, Peterson produced a diverse body of work that she exhibited at various institutions such as Société des Artistes Francais, Saint Botolph Club in Boston, the Art Institute of Chicago and in 1915 at the Panama Pacific International Exposition in San Francisco. In 1916, Peterson, after visiting the pacific Northwest with artist and friend Louis Comfort Tiffany, frequented the various art colonies that dotted the Massachusetts coast line including the one at Edgartown on Martha's Vineyard.

Peterson's works of beach and pier scenes executed during her stays at the art colonies along the New England shore "figure prominently during this period, exquisitely capturing Americans on holiday." (P.J. Pierce in *Jane Peterson: An American Artist*, p. 32) *On the Pier, Edgartown*, executed during her stay on Martha's Vineyard, portrays a lively parade of promenaders and beach goers strolling along the pier having recently disembarked from an island ferry. Employing grand brush strokes and assertive line, Peterson creates a tapestried or mosaic effect of highly expressive tones of blue pink and yellow offset by pure, glowing whites. By 1916, Peterson's style had become very definitive which has been described in followng way: " her linear construction directed a viewer along a definite course and did not allow the viewer's attention to wander. Her tonal masses dominated lines and defined form, while subtle, thin oscillating lines emphasized form edges to better display the juxtapositioning of dark and light color areas. In some ways, Peterson's paintings resemble cloisonné, in that color is often surrounded by a thin outlining of charcoal or contrasting paint much like the thin wires of cloisonné surround enamel. However, lines do not encompass or totally contain color areas, but combine in a grand decorative order and show control in carefreeness. The work of Peterson becomes a sensuous place in the commonplace movements of nature." (*Jane Peterson: An American Artist*, p. 17)

The innovative stylistic elements displayed in *On the Pier, Edgartown* were the quintessential characteristics of Peterson's painting that achieved critical acclaim. One reviewer in 1917 noted: "Miss Jane Peterson uses strong colors and a broad brush to give the facts about docks and fishing craft and harbors in a somewhat knock-you-down fashion." (as quoted in *Jane Peterson: An American Artist*, p. 32)

Estimate: $300,000-500,000

•79

JANE PETERSON (1876–1965)
Venice Canal
signed 'Jane Peterson' (lower right)
oil on canvas
24 x 18 in. (61 x 45.7 cm.)

Estimate: $40,000–60,000

80

•80

JOHN SLOAN (1871-1951)
Grassy Dunes, Gloucester
signed and dated 'John Sloan 1914' (lower left)
oil on canvas
20 x 24 in. (50.8 x 61 cm.)

PROVENANCE:
The Studio Group, Inc.
Parke-Bernet, New York, April 19, 1968, lot 90A
Christie's, New York, January 29, 1980, lot 488

LITERATURE:
R. Elzea, *John Sloan's Oil Paintings: A Catalogue Raisonné*, Part One,
Newark, Delaware, 1991, p. 144, no. 277

Estimate: $30,000-50,000

•81

FREDERICK CARL FRIESEKE (1874-1939)

On the Beach

signed 'F. C. Frieseke' (lower right)

oil on canvas

32 x 32 in. (81.3 x 81.3 cm.)

PROVENANCE:

Vose Galleries, Inc., Boston, Massachusetts.

Private Collection, Dallas, Texas.

By descent in the family to the present owner.

EXHIBITED:

Paris, France, Salon de la Société Nationale des Beaux-Arts, 1913, no. 481 or 484

Albuquerque, New Mexico, University of New Mexico Art Gallery, *Impressionism in America*, February-March 1965, no. 11, illusrtrated (This exhibition also traveled to San Francisco, California, De Young Museum, March-May 1965)

Savannah, Georgia, The Telfair Academy of Arts and Sciences, *Frederick Frieseke, 1874-1939*, November-December 1974, no. 8, pp. 16-17, illustrated, as *Girl in Blue* (This work also traveled to Raleigh, North Carolina, The North Carolina Museum of Art, February-March 1975; St. Petersburg, Florida, Museum of Fine Arts, April-May 1975; Columbia, South Carolina, Columbia Museum of Art, May-June 1975)

New York, Berry-Hill Galleries, *Frederick C. Frieseke: Women in Repose*, May-June 1990, no. 10, illustrated

LITERATURE:

"A Summer's Day", *LIFE Magazine*, July 23, 1965, illustrated, as *Girl in Blue*

RELATED WORKS:

On The Beach, oil on canvas, 32¼ x 32¼ in. (82.2 x 82.2 cm.), Private collection

Frederick Carl Frieseke's body of work executed between 1904 and 1919 represent the artist's most ambitious and important forays into Impressionism. Residing in Giverny, Frieseke devoted himself to painting as a "true Impressionist" who "laid aside all accepted rules of painting...and went to nature." (Clara MacChesney, "Frederick Carl Frieseke—His Works and Suggestions for Painting from Nature," *Arts and Decorations* 3, November 1912, pp. 13 -15 as quoted in M. M. Domit, *Frederick Frieseke*, Savannah, Georgia, 1974, pp. 8-9) The inspiration for the majority of Frieseke's paintings during this period in Giverny was his lush garden, eclectic house and other serene areas located in close proximity. In the winter of 1913, the artist traveled to Corsica, a trip which inspired a small body of work that were set on the island's beaches and included the model, Marcelle, both in the nude and fully clothed holding a parasol. *On the Beach*, a work from this series illustrates in both subject and style the artist's most acclaimed characteristics.

Central to Frieseke's works is his passion for depicting sunlight. In an interview in 1914, the artist explains this interest: "No, it is sunshine, flowers in sunshine; girls in sunshine; the nude in sunshine, which I have been principally interested in. If I could only reproduce it exactly as I see it I would be satisfied." ("Frederick Carl Frieseke," p. 15) Frieseke's study of sunlight resulted in the application of various tones and hues of the most ingenious combinations. In his paintings, he employs a broken yet sophisticated and controlled brushwork, from which an overall pattern emerges composed of light and dark and color juxtapositions, creating a rhythmic harmony that is pervasive throughout an entire work. Recurrent in Frieseke's most important works is the use of a single woman who functions as the catalyst for these stylistic elements. *On the Beach* includes the solitary model, Marcelle, listfully standing on the expansive Corsican beach holding an opened parasol with the ebbing tide beyond. The entire picture is saturated with the Mediterranean sun which creates deep and resounding contrasts of light and dark that modulates the surface of painting. Frieseke portrays with great skill these contrasts using varying tones of blues and whites as seen in the model's dress and her own shadow, the small wells in the trodden beach and in the ripples of the sea. Frieseke's *On the Beach* though his choice of color, light and brushwork transforms into an intricate pattern of undulating line and curvilinear shapes that resonate throughout the entire canvas.

Away from the private enclave of his house and gardens in Giverny, Frieseke in *On the Beach* maintains his passionate investigation of sunlight, color and pattern. Unlike the moist, dappled light Frieseke encountered in Giverny, the unrelenting sun of Corsica afforded the artist with a different visual sensation and emotion which he embraced with enthusiasm. Frieseke in an 1914 interview stated: "In making an impression from nature one should never consider time or method, but only the result. One should never forget that seeing and producing an effect of nature which is beautiful is not a matter of intellect but of feeling." ("Frederick Carl Frieseke," p. 14) *On the Beach* through its vivid color, light and texture evokes a response that is not borne from the mind, but from the heart— a reaction that is elemental to his most successful works.

This work will be included in the forthcoming *catalogue raisonné* of Frieseke's work being compiled by Nicholas Kilmer, the artist's grandson.

Estimate: $600,000-800,000

81

•82

CHILDE HASSAM (1859-1935)

Confirmation Day

signed and dated 'Childe Hassam. 1889' (lower right)

oil on canvas

15 x 18 in. (38.1 x 45.7 cm.)

PROVENANCE:

Sale: American Art Association, New York, *Paintings Belonging to Mr. P. Chock*, March 9, 1898, no. 172 (possibly).
Hirschl & Adler Galleries, Inc., New York.
Christie's, New York, May 29, 1987, lot 170.
Acquired by the present owner from the above.

EXHIBITED:

New York, Hirschl & Adler Galleries, Inc., *American Art from the Gallery's Collection*, October 1980, no. 56, illustrated
East Hampton, New York, Guild Hall Museum, *Childe Hassam 1859-1935*, March-May 1981, no. 3

France in the 1880s attracted a host of American artists seeking to immerse themselves in the ways of Impressionism. While still in his twenties, Childe Hassam became a part of this migration in 1886, when the artist and his wife settled in Paris. They remained there for the next three years. During this period, Hassam painted *Confirmation Day*, which was inspired by the street life of Paris that had, during his sojourn there, become the central theme of his art. With passages of broken brushwork, and a sophisticated command of color, atmosphere and light, *Confirmation Day* represents one of Hassam's early successful forays into Impressionism.

Hassam moved to Paris with the intent of "refining his talent in the larger crucible of contemporary art." (D.F. Hoopes, *Childe Hassam*, New York, 1982, p. 13) While in Paris, Hassam began his studies at the Academie Julian. However, his experience at the school was not entirely to his liking, finding more routine and conformity in its method than innovation. In time he would reject it altogether, and by 1888, Hassam stopped attending the Academy to develop the tenets of Impressionism on his own.

Already his style had began to exhibit a shift away from the more tonal approach evident in the works from his earlier, Boston period. While embracing aspects of Impressionism, Hassam never fully considered himself one of the Impressionists. Donaldson F. Hoopes describes the development of Hassam's distinctive style: "If the search for the equivalent in paint of the light of nature involved borrowing some of the Impressionist's innovations, then he borrowed, but at no time in his career did Hassam subordinate the emotional content of the represented image to a supremacy of color or technique. Indeed, most of his paintings from the Paris years also tell of his search for a synthesis of his commitment to realism and the demands of a viable plastic expression." (*Childe Hassam*, p. 13). In an interview later in his career, Hassam would elaborate on the tenets of his style: "Art, to me, is the interpretation of the impression which nature makes upon the eye and brain. The word impression' as applied to art has been used, and in the general acceptance of the term has become perverted. It really means the only truth because it means going straight to nature for inspiration, and not allowing tradition to dictate to your brush, or to put it brown, green or some other colored spectacles between you and nature as it really exists. The true impressionism is realism." (A.E. Ives, "Talks with Artists: Childe Hassam on Painting Street Scenes," *Art Amateur*, 27 October 1892, p. 117).

Confirmation Day captures Hassam's innovative melding of contemporary styles, and his fascination with the everyday scenes unfolding around him. As one art historian notes, "Hassam's greatest amusement was to wander about the streets of Paris in search of motifs for his paintings.... [He] developed in these Paris scenes a working catalogue of themes....More than professional duty, we sense in the process of accumulation the drive of personal curiosity, a faith in the artistic process as a genuine search for truth, and a belief that his role as artist observer was to discover and communicate the often unrecognized aspects of life." (U.W. Hiesinger, *Childe Hassam, American Impressionist*, New York, 1994, pp. 42-6)

In *Confirmation Day* the artist depicts a momentary vignette, the procession along a Parisian street of a nun leading a boy and two girls, the latter arrayed in their white confirmation dresses. Energized through a lively brush stroke, color, light and atmosphere, the work of art is infused with a restrained sense of movement, indicative of a quieter outlying neighborhood of the city. The day is overcast, and the buildings and street are broadly painted in muted tones overlaid with a rich color scheme of pinks, reds, lavenders, blues and greens. Applying his inimitable style to an urban view, Hassam brings together the essential elements which would come to define his greatest achievements in American Impressionism.

Ulrich Hiesinger offers the following conclusion to Hassam's three-year visit: "On leaving Paris, [he] had every reason to feel satisfied with his accomplishments. He could claim to have undergone the rigors of French academic training, had succeeded in exhibiting at the Salon in each of the three years of his stay—no ordinary feat for a young painter—and capped this by receiving a medal at the Exposition Universelle...Hassam had seen his name and reputation steadily increase at home. He received admiring attention in art journals and press reviews. He had even managed to keep selling his work all the while. If he was still not well known, let alone famous, he had certainly moved far beyond the small world of Boston to join the international ranks of professionals worthy of serious attention." (*Childe Hassam, American Impressionist*, p. 58)

This painting will be included in Stuart P. Feld's and Kathleen M. Burnside's forthcoming *catalogue raisonné* of the artist's work.

Estimate: $400,000-600,000

82

83

VARIOUS PROPERTIES

•83

HENRY OSSAWA TANNER (1859-1937)
Shepherd with Herd
signed 'H.O. Tanner' (lower left)
oil on board
18⅛ x 24 in. (46 x 61 cm.)

Estimate: $20,000-30,000

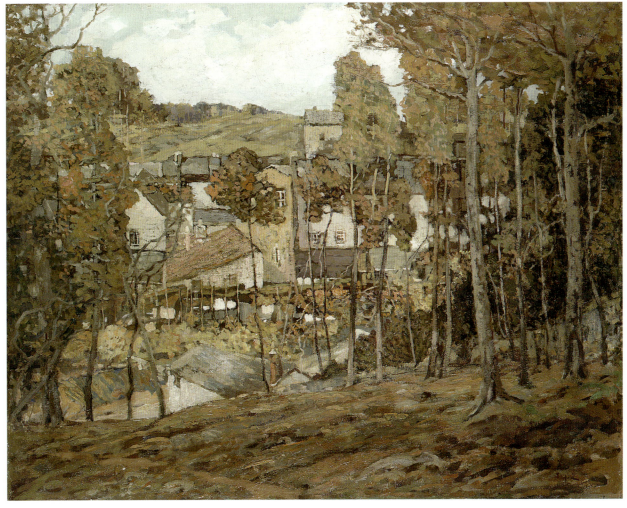

84

•84

WALTER ELMER SCHOFIELD (1867-1944)

A Cornish Village
signed 'Schofield' (lower right)
oil on canvas
38 x 48 in. (96.5 x 122 cm.)

EXHIBITED:
Pittsburgh, Pennsylvania, Carnegie Institute, *Tenth Annual Exhibition*, November 1905-January 1906, no. 235
Chadds Ford, Pennsylvania, Brandywine River Museum, *Walter Elmer Schofield*, September-November 1983
Allentown, Pennsylvania, Allentown Art Museum, *Pennsylvania School of Landscape Painting: An Original American Impressionism*, September-November 1984, p. 47, illustrated (This exhibition also traveled to Washington, DC, Corcoran Gallery of Art, December 1984-February 1985; Greensburg, Pennsylvania, Westmoreland Museum of Art, March-May 1985; Chadds Ford, Pennsylvania, Brandywine River Museum, June-September 1985)

Estimate: $40,000-60,000

85

•85

WALTER LAUNT PALMER (1854-1932)
Snow-Laden
signed 'W.L. Palmer.' (lower right)
oil on canvas
24½ x 34¾ in. (62.2 x 38.3 cm.)

EXHIBITED:
New York, National Academy of Design, *Annual Exhibition*, 1897, no. 129
New York, The American Art Galleries, *Second Annual Exhibition of the Society of Landscape Painters*, May 1900, no. 78, pp. 46-47, illustrated, as *Morning After the Snow*

LITERATURE:
Modern Culture, Cleveland, Ohio, April 1901
M. Mann, *Walter Launt Palmer: Poetic Reality*, Exton, Pennsylvania, 1984, pp. 79, 125, no. 335, illustrated, as *Morning After the Snow*

Estimate: $40,000-60,000

86

•86

EDWARD WILLIS REDFIELD (1869-1965)
Canal Boat in Winter
signed 'E.W. Redfield' (lower right)
oil on canvas
26¼ x 32¼ in. (66.6 x 82 cm.)

LITERATURE:
T.C. Folk, *The Pennsylvania Impressionists*, 1997, Cranbury, New
Jersey, pp. 44-45, illustrated

Estimate: $80,000-120,000

•87

CHILDE HASSAM (1859-1935)

The Toll Bridge, New Hampshire Near Exeter

signed and dated 'Childe Hassam 1906' (lower left)
oil on canvas
20 x 30 in. (50.8 x 76.2 cm.)

PROVENANCE:
American Academy of Arts and Letters, New York, bequest of the artist.
The Milch Galleries, New York.
John Fox, Boston, Massachusetts.
Babcock Galleries, New York.
Meredith Long and Company, Houston, Texas.
Esther F. Goodrich, Houston, Texas.
Goodrich Foundation, Houston, Texas.
Peter Benzinger.
Coe Kerr Galleries, New York.
Terry DeLapp Galleries, Los Angeles, California.
Private Collection, Texas.
Christie's, New York, May 29, 1987, lot 203
Acquired by the present owner from the above.

EXHIBITED:
New York, Babcock Galleries, *Childe Hassam*, 1960, no. 16

Childe Hassam paints *The Toll Bridge, New Hampshire Near Exeter* with the quick application of lively brush strokes characteristic of his impressionist style after 1900. He develops patterns of broken brushwork in the clouds, trees, and water, all rendered in a bright palette. The composition is dominated by an wooden bridge near Exeter, New Hampshire. For many years a painter of picturesque locales throughout New England, Hassam's choice of the toll bridge as his subject compares, for example, to his famous, later landscape, *The Bridge at Old Lyme* of 1908 (Georgia Museum of Art, Athens, Georgia)—which likewise depicts a timbered structure of substantial age.

Hassam was long familiar with the region of coastal New Hampshire depicted here, for the area is close to one of Hassam's most celebrated summer haunts—the Isles of Shoals, and the home of Celia Thaxter, a noted poet and journalist whose salon at Appledore was frequented by numerous artists and writers over several decades. Hassam regularly visited the island from the mid-1880s until 1916.

Very likely, *The Toll Bridge, New Hampshire, Near Exeter* was painted by Hassam in August of 1906, when he is known to have stopped at the Isles of Shoals on an extended tour of New England. That summer was one of restless travel for Hassam. "I am the Marco Polo of the painters," he wrote to his friend Florence Griswold. The art-historian Ulrich Hiesinger adds that in 1906 "at times it seems that he positively disliked staying in one place," visiting that summer Florence Griswold in Old Lyme and J. Alden Weir in Branchville (both in Connecticut), stopping at the Isles of Shoals in August, before continuing on to two other towns, and finally Old Lyme again for the autumn months. (U. Hiesinger, *Childe Hassam, American Impressionist*, New York, 1994, p. 131)

During 1906, Hassam's artistic output tended to consist of landscapes and rural subjects over urban ones. *The Toll Bridge, New Hampshire Near Exeter* in its substantial scale and highly developed, patterned surface, serves as a superlative example of the artist's landscapes from this period, and conveys the full vision of Hassam's lively, impressionist style.

This painting will be included in Stuart P. Feld's and Kathleen M. Burnside's forthcoming *catalogue raisonné* of the artist's work.

Estimate: $400,000-600,000

87

88

•88

JOHN SLOAN (1871-1951)
Orchard Wall
signed 'John Sloan' (lower right)—inscribed twice with title
on the stretcher
oil on canvas
20 x 24 in. (50.8 x 61 cm.)

PROVENANCE:
Reverend Robert T. Dunn.
Kennedy Galleries, Inc., New York.

EXHIBITED:
New York, Hudson Guild, *Exhibition of Paintings, Etchings and
Drawings by John Sloan*, February-April 1916, no. 18
New York, Kennedy Galleries, Inc., *Sixty American Paintings 1840-
1980*, April-May 1908, no. 24, illustrated
New York, Owen Gallery, *The Eight*, April-June 1997

LITERATURE:
R. Elzea, *John Sloan's Oil Paintings: A Catalogue Raisonné*, Newark,
Delaware, 1991, no. 291, p. 147, illustrated.

Estimate: $40,000-60,000

89

•89

EDWARD WILLIS REDFIELD (1869–1965)

Aetna Valley

signed 'E.W. Redfield' (lower right)—signed again and inscribed with title on the stretcher

oil on canvas

26 x 32 in. (66 x 81.2 cm.)

This painting will be included in the forthcoming *catalogue raisonné* of Edward Redfield's works being compiled by Dr. Thomas Folk.

Estimate: $60,000–80,000

•90

MAURICE BRAZIL PRENDERGAST (1859-1924)

Viewing the Sailboats

signed 'Prendergast' (lower right)

oil on canvas

15⅜ x 20⅞ in. (39 x 50.5 cm.)

PROVENANCE:
Estate of the artist.
Charles Prendergast, 1924.
Mrs. Charles B. Prendergast, 1948.
Coe Kerr Gallery, Inc., New York.

EXHIBITED:
New York, Coe Kerr Gallery, Inc., *American Impressionism II*, May-June 1989, illustrated

LITERATURE:
C. Clark, N.M. Mathews and G. Owens, *Maurice Brazil Prendergast and Charles Prendergast: A Catalogue Raisonné*, Williamstown, Massachusetts, 1990, p. 249, no. 163, illustrated

Viewing the Sailboats is a brilliant example of Maurice Prendergast's unique style: a combination of color theory-derived from the French Impressionists, and varied brushstroke. In this wonderfully decorative painting Prendergast applied his self-taught technique to a motif that became a recurring theme throughout his career.

Prendergast was fascinated with the leisure activities of the new middle class at the turn of the century. Often observing crowds from a distance enjoying a promenade along the coast or through the park, Prendergast accumulated numerous sketchbooks and watercolors of these recreational scenes. These on-site sketches and watercolors were the primary basis for Prendergast's oils where his experimentation with color and form is most apparent.

Prendergast traveled abroad extensively throughout his career and appreciated the work of his European contemporaries such as C/aezanne, Matisse and Seurat. He embraced their brilliant color palette, conceding to color and brushstroke alone as a means of representation. Prendergast ". . . varied the brushstroke to suit the object represented: a twirl of a full brush for a parasol, a few broad strokes within a contour line for a female figure." (H. H.l Rhys, *Maurice Prendergast*, Cambridge, 1960, p. 42) In *Viewing the Sailboats* the viewer's eye is drawn to the brilliant pink of the woman's dress and the purple splash of the gentleman's top hat. These patches of color weave a pattern of movement across the canvas, emphasizing the motion of the holiday scene.

At the time this painting was executed Prendergast was experimenting with varied brushstroke throughout the canvas. "He transformed the regularity of the glowing, rich spots and dabs of color into irregular and curvilinear shaped patterns, brushstroke overlapping brushstroke..." (R. J. Wattenmaker, *Maurice Prendergast*, New York, 1994, p. 100) In *Viewing the Sailboats*, the rhythm of the brushstrokes in the foreground contrast sharply with the more controlled, horizontal brushstrokes in the sea and sky. The contrast of color and brushstroke emphasizes the three distinct horizontal bands within the picture: the shoreline, the sea and the sky. The soaring verticality of the trees interlocks the three horizontal forms. By using this array of devices Prendergast emphasizes the flatness of the surface heightening the overall decorative effect. *Viewing the Sailboats* exemplifies the self-taught style of Maurice Prendergast by merging several devices he favored throughout his career, experimentation with color and brushstroke applied to one of his favorite motifs, a promenade along the coast.

Estimate: $200,000-300,000

90

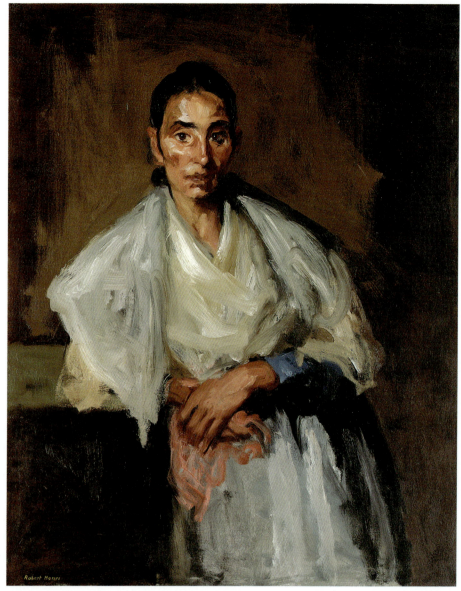

91

PROPERTY FROM
THE COLLECTION OF ROBERT S. LEE, SR.

•91

ROBERT HENRI (1865-1929)

Gypsy

signed 'Robert Henri' (lower left)

oil on canvas

40¾ x 32¾ in. (103.5 x 83.2 cm.)

PROVENANCE:

John C. Le Clair, New Jersey.

Julian J. Foss.

Sotheby's, New York, December 6, 1984, lot 173.

John Post Lee, August 1988

Estimate: $40,000-60,000

VARIOUS PROPERTIES

•92

LEON SCHULMAN GASPARD (1882-1964)

La Ville de Pauvres: A Triptych

the first: signed 'Schulman Gaspar' and inscribed 'Russe' (lower left); the second: signed 'L Schulman Gaspar' and inscribed 'Russe' and dated '1912' (lower left)—signed 'Leon S Gaspard' and inscribed with title on an old label attached to the reverse; the third: signed 'Schulman Gaspar' (lower right)

each: oil on canvasboard

the first: 12⅞ x 9⅜ (32.7 x 23.8 cm.); the second: 12⅞ x 16⅛ in. (32.7 x 41 cm.); the third: 12⅞ x 9⅜ in. (32.7 x 23.8 cm.)

Estimate: $80,000-120,000

92

•93

FREDERICK CARL FRIESEKE (1874-1939)

Woman with Jewels

oil on canvas
32 x 32 in. (81.3 x 81.3 cm.)

While the expansive gardens and landscapes of Giverny provided much of Frieseke's subject matter, he occasionally transposed his outdoor light and color into more intimate settings. Often, Frieseke experimented with contrasting patterns, further incorporating into his canvases various designs seen on furniture, wallpaper, and fabric, as he does with the interior setting and the pink dress which appear in the present work, *Women with Jewels*. As William H. Gerdts points out, "it was Frieseke who introduced into the repertory of Giverny painting the concern for rich, decorative patterns, related to the art of Edouard Vuillard, Pierre Bonnard, and the other Nabi painters." (*Monet's Giverny: An Impressionist Colony*, New York, 1993, p. 172)

This painting will be inlcuded in the forthcoming *catalogue raisonné* of Frieseke's work being compiled by Nicholas Kilmer, the artist's grandson.

Estimate: $200,000-300,000

93

•94

MARY CASSATT (1844-1926)

Portrait of an Italian Lady

signed 'M.S. Cassatt' (lower left)

oil on canvas

31¾ x 23½ (80.7 x 57.1 cm.)

PROVENANCE:

Jacques Speiss, Paris, France.
Parke-Bernet, New York, March 10, 1971, lot 40.

EXHIBITED:

Washington, DC, National Gallery of Art, *Mary Cassatt*, no. 17, illustrated

Isetan, Japan, Museum of Art, *The Art of Mary Cassatt*, 1981-82, no. 8, illustrated (This exhibition also traveled to Nara, Japan, Prefectural Museum of Art)

Memphis, Tennessee, Dixon Gallery and Gardens, *Degas and His Friends*, 1986, no. 14, illustrated

LITERATURE:

A.D. Breeskin, *Mary Cassatt: A Catalogue Raisonné of the Oils, Pastels, Watercolors and Drawings*, Washington, DC, 1970, no. 938, p. 305, illustrated

N.M. Mathews, *Mary Cassatt*, New York, 1987, pp. 32, 43, illustrated *Cassatt: A Retrospective*, N.M. Mathews, Ed., New York, 1996, p. 91, illustrated

Mary Cassatt's *Portrait of an Italian Lady*, painted approximately one year after her transition from academic work into the more modern style of Impressionism, is much more than an ordinary portrait in the Impressionist style. It is a classic example of the intuitive approach to her sitters that Cassatt executed with great skill throughout her career. For Cassatt, the involvement of the sitter is an integral part of the picture. Evident in almost all of Cassatt's work, the pensive mood and penetrating gaze of the sitter signify her engagement beyond the realm of the portrait. The lively brushstroke and dramatic color scheme, and the diagonal motion that extends from the sitter's face and to beyond the left margin of the composition, make this work a superb example of Impressionism.

After struggling for almost a decade for recognition in the established Paris Salon, Mary Cassatt eagerly accepted Edgar Degas's invitation to join him in exhibiting her work with the other members of the Impressionist group. While they have become known as Impressionists, in the late nineteenth century, they "preferred to be called 'Independents'" (N.M. Mathews, *Mary Cassatt*, New York, 1987, p. 37). The term "Independents" is significant as it implies a forceful and noble rejection of the starched Parisian art world in favor of purely autonomous conduct. In fact, "Reminiscing thirty-five years after the fact, Cassatt still had strong feeling about the decision; in 1912 she told her biographer, Achille Segard, 'I accepted with joy. I hated conventional art. I began to live.' Clearly, she recalled the years of trying to find her way in the labyrinthe art world of the 1870s, juggling the demands of her conservative American milieu, official taste, and her own independence, as a dark period, and she considered it the turning point of her life when, at the age of thirty-three she was given the opportunity to paint and exhibit freely." (*Mary Cassatt*, p. 37).

Cassatt's artistic output changed dramatically as soon as she made the bold shift to Impressionism. Her works immediately took on a more daring character. *Portrait of an Italian Lady*, executed circa 1878 is just one example of the type of work that burst from Cassatt's imagination as soon as she was freed from the conventions of the Paris Salon. "In *Portrait of an Italian Lady* Cassatt adds to the informal pose and the use of white and pastel colors a psychological element typical of Impressionist figure studies. With head tilted and eyelids lowered, the subject seems to be listening to or watching something outside the picture's limits, and this gives the viewer the feeling of having happened on the scene, of sharing with the artist the role of observer." (*Mary Cassatt*, p. 43) This work is a brilliant example of the principles of Impressionism applied with Cassatt's zest, creativity and intelligence. It clearly illustrates why she was considered "one of the most intelligent interpreters of the new art outside the original circle." (*Mary Cassatt*, p. 37)

While Cassatt's style was changing dramatically at this time, she was also adding an element of intimacy to her subjects. Classic in the work of the Impressionists, Cassatt presents her viewers with a series of contradictions in her presentation of the real world. The serious gaze of the sitter is fixed on an unknown object or activity, or perhaps her mind wanders in contemplation. However, her look is not somber, in fact, there is the trace of a smile on her lips. Furthermore, the colorful setting would seem to preclude a grave situation. Like other artist's, Cassatt's "subjects [were] drawn from the world around [her] with an ironic eye, [and] displayed a fragile balance between the public and the private, discretion and indiscretion, beauty and ugliness. A rigid or uninformed viewer could easily be confused by the transient and shifting effects of this style and, with some justification, feel mocked by these sophisticated artists. However, Cassatt was intellectually nimble and prided herself on her own penetrating opinions on art and society. From her very first efforts to incorporate Impressionist devices into her work she was fascinated with the aesthetic power of a painting's successful balance of contradictory elements." (*Mary Cassatt*, p. 40)

It is rare that an artist's earliest pursuits with a new medium or philosophy are as accomplished as Cassatt's earliest forays into Impressionism. Cassatt's first products in what was to become her celebrated style and technique not only foreshadow the magnificent body of work that she would produce for the rest of her career, but they reflect her innate artistic ability. While the Impressionists' early exhibitions were not universally praised by art critics, a number of Cassatt's works were commended. *Portrait of an Italian Lady* is certainly the type of work that spurred critics to take notice of her and write as follows: "It is equally impossible to visit the exhibition without finding most interesting Mlle. Cassatt's portraits. An utterly remarkable... sense of elegance and distinction marks these portraits. Mlle. Cassatt *deserves very special attention...*" (L. Duranty, "The Fourth Exhibition by a Group of Independent Artists," *La Chronique des arts et de la curiosité*, April 19, 1879, as quoted in *Mary Cassatt: A Retrospective*, N.M. Mathews, Ed., New York, 1996, p. 124) This painting will be included in the Cassatt Committee's revision of Adelyn Dohme Breeskin's *catalogue raisonné* of the works of Mary Cassatt.

Estimate: $700,000-1,000,000

94

95

•95

EDWARD HENRY POTTHAST (1857-1927)

On the Beach

signed 'E Potthast' (lower right)—signed 'Edward H. Potthast' and inscribed with title on a label attached to the reverse

oil on canvasboard

8 x 9¾ in. (20.3 x 24.8cm.)

This painting will be included in Mary O'Connell's forthcoming *catalogue raisonné* of the artist's work.

Estimate: $30,000-50,000

96

•96

THEODORE EARL BUTLER (1861-1936)
Plum Tree in the Artist's Garden
signed 'T.E. Butler' (lower right)
oil on canvas
25¾ x 21¾ in. (65.4 x 55.3 cm.)
This work will be included in Patrick Bertrand's forthcoming
catalogue raisonné of the work of Theodore Earl Butler.

Estimate: $40,000-60,000

•97

FRANK WESTON BENSON (1862-1951)

Dawn on the York

signed and dated 'F.W. Benson '31' (lower right)
oil on canvas laid down on cradled masonite
40 x 50 in. (101.6 x 127 cm.)

LITERATURE:

B.W. Chambers, "Frank W. Benson: Unity and Diversification in the Development of an Artistic Style" in
Frank W. Benson: A Retrospective, New York, 1989, pp. 158-159, illustrated

In the late 1920s and early 1930s Frank Weston Benson traveled to New Brunswick, Canada to paint a series of
oil paintings and watercolors that depicted salmon fishing on the York River. In these works the artist
combined his brilliant Impressionist technique with subjects similar to great sporting pictures such as Winslow
Homer's Adirondack watercolors. An avid outdoorsman and sportsman, Benson was attracted to this rugged
subject matter. *Dawn on the York* captures the essence of these two qualities—the painting is infused with careful
observation of light, color and atmosphere, and it speaks to the artist's understanding of the peacefulness and
tranquility found in the North American wilderness.

In the sporting subjects that Benson completed after 1900, he retained the Impressionist style that had won him
wide acclaim earlier in his career. The surface of the canvas of *Dawn on the York* is animated with vigorous
brushwork. Cool blues and grays are placed side by side to give the effect of dawn's early light shimmering off
the surface of the water. On the far horizon a streak of salmon-colored sky is juxtaposed with a deep royal
blue—a brilliant Impressionist use of color that recalls his virtuoso canvases executed on North Haven Island off
the coast of Maine.

Of Benson's sporting paintings from this period Bruce Chambers writes, "In 1930-31, Benson completed tow
of his finest sporting oils, near pendants in subject and mood. *Twilight*, the earlier of the two, shows a lone
canoeman on a mountain lake, silhouetted against the fading light that glances off the water. *Dawn on the York*
of a year later is no less imposing a painting, its deep purples, greens, and lavenders arrested at the horizon by a
brilliant streak of orange. In both works, the painter shapes his composition in broad, flat patterns; the motif is
Winslow Homer's and the underlying aesthetic is still deeply ingrained in the Western tradition, but the effect
is astonishingly Oriental." (*Frank W. Benson: A Retrospective*, New York, 1989, p. 158)

As an Impressionist, Benson was fascinated with atmospheric effects of various times of day. Faith Andrews
Bedford writes, "Benson loved to paint at dawn. The titles of many works reveal his fascination with the pale
light of early morning. In his younger days hunting on the marshes near Salem with his brothers and Dan
Henderson, Benson had spent many a chilly hour waiting for the sun to rise and the birds to fly. As a painter
the luminous quality of early morning challenged him time and again." (*Frank W. Benson: American Impressionist*,
p. 201) This painting will be included in the forthcoming *catalogue raisonné* of the artist's work being compiled
by Sheila Dugan and Vose Galleries of Boston.

Estimate: $300,000-500,000

97

98

PROPERTY OF MR. AND MRS. GEORGE BERMAN

•98

ARTHUR BEECHER CARLES (1882-1952)
Still Life with Summer Flowers
signed 'Carles' (upper right)
oil on canvas
32 x 36in. (81.2 x 91.5cm.)

Estimate: $40,000-60,000

99

•99

ARTHUR BEECHER CARLES (1882-1952)
Still Life with Flowers
signed 'Carles' on the reverse
oil on canvas
25¼ x 20½in. (64.2 x 52cm.)

Estimate: $20,000–30,000

100

VARIOUS PROPERTIES

•100

CHARLES EPHRAIM BURCHFIELD (1893-1967)
Wind Swept Trees
stamped with artist's estate stamp and numbered '15' (lower right)
watercolor, pencil, pastel and charcoal on paper laid down on board
33 x 39¾ in. (83.8 x 101 cm.)

Estimate: $80,000-120,000

101

•101

CHARLES EPHRAIM BURCHFIELD (1893-1967)

Forest Ravine

stamped with estate stamp and numbered '26' (lower left)—dated 'April 1, 1917' on the reverse
watercolor, pastel and gouache on paper laid down on board
22 x 18 in. (55.9 x 45.8 cm.)

PROVENANCE:
Frank K.M. Rehn Galleries, Inc., New York.

LITERATURE:
J.S. Trovato, *Charles Burchfield: Catalogue of Paintings in Public and Private Collections*, Utica, New York, 1970, no. 274, p. 58

Estimate: $30,000-50,000

102

•102

CHARLES EPHRAIM BURCHFIELD (1893-1967)

Sunflower

signed and dated 'Chas. Burchfield Aug. 15 1915' (lower
right)—inscribed 'Summer 1915' on the reverse
watercolor and pencil on paper
20 x 14 in. (50.8 x 35.6 cm.)

PROVENANCE:
Mr. and Mrs. A.R. Gurney, Jr.
A. Conger Goodyear.
Dr. Stephen Goodyear, New York.
Christie's, New York, December 7, 1984, lot 327.
Acquired by the present owner from the above.

LITERATURE:
J.S. Trovato, *Charles Burchfield: Catalogue of Paintings in Public and
Private Collections*, Utica, New York, 1970, pp. 33-34, illustrated

Estimate: $30,000-50,000

103

•103

CHARLES EPHRAIM BURCHFIELD (1893-1967)

Russian Giant Sunflower

signed with artist's monogram and dated '1940' (lower right)—inscribed with title and dated again on the original backing attached to the reverse
pastel and watercolor on paper laid down on board
28 x 24 in. (71.1 x 61 cm.)

EXHIBITED:
New York, Owen Gallery, *Modernism: Am American View*, May–June 1994

LITERATURE:
J.S. Trovato, *Charles Burchfield: Catalogue of Paintings in Public and Private Collections*, Utica, New York, 1970, no. 935, p. 190

Estimate: $50,000–70,000

104

•104

REGINALD MARSH (1898-1954)

Atomic Blonde

signed and dated 'Reginald Marsh 1952' (lower right)

ink and pencil on paper

22¼ x 30⅞ in. (56.5 x 78.4 cm.)

PROVENANCE:

Vincent Price, Los Angeles, California.

Bernard Danenberg Galleries, Inc., New York.

Estimate: $25,000-35,000

105

•105

REGINALD MARSH (1889-1954)
Window Shopping, New York
oil on canvas
42 x 34in. (106.7 x 86.4cm.)

PROVENANCE:
Senator William Benton, New York

EXHIBITED:
Rome, Italy, Galeria Netta Vespignani, *Realism in New York in the Thirties*, May, 1990, illus.

This work was executed in 1934.

Estimate: $40,000-60,000

106

•106

THOMAS HART BENTON (1889-1975)

Fisherman at Sunset

signed 'Benton' (lower left)—dated '1943' and inscribed
with various notations on the reverse
watercolor and gouache on paper
16½ x 22¾ in. (41.9 x 57.8 cm.)

PROVENANCE:
Maurice J. Liederman, New York, gift from the artist.
By descent in the family to the present owner.

As the twentieth century's champion of rural America, Thomas
Hart Benton regularly portrayed the honest and hardworking
people that he met during his travels throughout the country.
From his earliest works on, he showed a keen interest in
rediscovering every aspect of the United States from his childhood.
After a rich period of achievement in the 1930s, the artist turned
to more contemporary and serious subject matter in the 1940s,
namely World War II. However, in contrast to the highly charged
paintings with overt political content that Benton painted at this
time, *Fisherman at Sunset* of 1943 is a tranquil glorification of
simple life in America.

At the height of Benton's career, Maynard Walker, a New York
art dealer with Kansas roots, lauded his art in a 1933 article in *Art
Digest* where he "contrasted [his] sturdy realism with the bizarre
eccentricities of the French modernists. ....[He went on to say that]
'One of the most significant things in the art world today is the
increasing importance of real American art. I mean an art which
really springs from American soil and seeks to interpret American
life... And very noticeably much of the most vital modern art in
America is coming out of our long backward Middle West.
Largely through the creative output of a few sincere and vital
painters, the East is learning that there is an America west of the

Alleghenies and that it is worth being put on canvas.'" (H. Adams,
Thomas Hart Benton, An American Original, New York, 1989, p.
217) Benton strayed little from this type of subject matter during
the course of his career. From paintings to mural commissions, he
used the same distinctly American iconography and themes to
express himself.

Fisherman at Sunset depicts Menemsha Lake in Martha's Vineyard,
and is a classic example of Benton's work as it succinctly describes
his absolute reverence for the working people of America. In his
characteristic style, having reduced his composition to a few key
elements and omitting all superfluous detail, Benton makes the
strongest impact upon his viewer. The fisherman, stooped and
pushing a boat, with his exaggerated hands, signifies the American
work ethic. The sun, circular and in the center of the composition,
presides serenely over the lake, far from the atrocities of the
Second World War.

It is no surprise that he returned time and again to depicting his
favorite icons as they were deeply connected to his ideology.
Henry Adams notes that as "much as he struggled to keep up with
the young soldiers, Benton felt most at home with the subjects of
an earlier period. Throughout the early forties, concurrently with
these war-related pictures, he continued to paint peaceful rural
subjects." (*Thomas Hart Benton, An American Original*, p. 316) This
work is yet another brilliant product of this passionate and often
outspoken artist, in his desire to express the "vigorously American
art he favored." (*Thomas Hart Benton, Drawings from Life*, p. 33)

Estimate: $70,000-100,000

107

•107

THOMAS HART BENTON (1889-1975)
Rock Rose and Daisy
signed 'Benton' (lower right)
oil on masonite
7¼ x 8¼ in. (18.4 x 21 cm.)

PROVENANCE:
Jeanne Liederman Klein, New York, gift from the artist.
By descent in the family to the present owner.

Estimate: $15,000–25,000

108

•108

THOMAS HART BENTON (1889-1975)
Lightning
signed 'Benton' (lower right)
oil on paperboard
6 x 9⅞ in. (15.2 x 25.2 cm.)

Estimate: $40,000-60,000

109

•109

JOHN STEUART CURRY (1897-1946)

Halt for the Night

signed 'John S. Curry' (lower right)
oil on canvas
22 x 30 in. (55.9 x 76.2 cm.)

PROVENANCE:
Constance Prosser Mellon, Ligonier, Pennsylvania.
By gift from the above to the present owner, 1975.

Estimate: $20,000–30,000

110

•110

BORIS LOVET-LORSKI (1894–1973)
'Rhythm', A Polished Bronze Figure
inscribed and dated 'B Lovet-Lorski 1924'
7⅞ in. (20 cm.) high

PROVENANCE:
Sotheby's, New York, December 4, 1986, lot 226

Estimate: $20,000–30,000

111

•111

PAUL MANSHIP (1885-1966)
'Europa and the Bull', A Parcel-Gilt Bronze Figural Group
inscribed 'P. MANSHIP © 1924' and 'ROMAN BRONZE
WORKS N- Y-'
11 in. (27.9 cm.) high, including a brown onyx base

PROVENANCE:
Frederic Crowninsheild, Boston, Massachusetts.
Private Collection, Massachusetts, by descent from the above.
Sotheby's, New York, November 29, 1990, lot 126.
Acquired by the present owner from the above.

LITERATURE:
P. Vitry, *Paul Manship, Sculpteur Americain*, Paris, France, 1927, pp.
45-47, illustration of another example in marble, titled *Europe et
Jupiter*

E. Murtha, *Paul Manship*, New York, 1957, pp. 15, 162-3, 179,
no. 169, pl. 31, illustration of another example
J.F. Hunter, G. Gittleson, L. Klein, S. Levy, *Paul Manship,
Changing Taste in America*, St. Paul, Minnesota, 1985, pp. 26-27,
no. 14, illustration of another example
J. Conner and J. Rosenkranz, *Rediscoveries in American Sculpture,
Studio Works, 1893-1939*, Austin, Texas, 1989, p. 140, illustration
of another example
J. Manship, *Paul Manship*, Washington, DC and London, 1989,
pp. 61-67, fig 56, illustration of another example
H. Rand, *Paul Manship*, Washington, DC, 1989, pp. 63-67,
illustration of another example

Europa and the Bull was cast by the Roman Bronze Works in an
edition of 20. Manship later enlarged and changed the model for
his marble version.

Estimate: $50,000-70,000

112

PROPERTY OF MR. AND MRS. GEORGE BERMAN

•112

STUART DAVIS (1894–1964)
Study for Eggbeater No. 3
signed 'Stuart Davis' (lower right)—signed again and
inscribed with title on the reverse
ink, gouache and pencil on paper
15¼ x 18¼ in. (38.8 x 46.3 cm.)

PROVENANCE:
The Downtown Gallery, New York.
Mr. Harris B. Steinberg, New York.
Robert Schoelkopf Gallery, New York.
Carlen Galleries, Philadelphia, Pennsylvania.
Acquired by the present owner from the above, 1972.

EXHIBITED:
Brooklyn, New York, The Brooklyn Museum, *Stuart Davis: Art
and Art Theory*, January-March, 1978, no. 16, illustrated (This
exhibition also traveled to Cambridge, Massachusetts, Fogg Art
Museum, April-May 1978)

This work will be included in the forthcoming *catalogue raisonné* of
the artist's work.

Estimate: $25,000-35,000

113

ANOTHER PROPERTY

•113

JOHN MARIN (1870-1953)
Region Huntington, Long Island
signed and dated 'Marin 52' (lower right)
oil on canvas
12 x 16 in. (30.5 x 40.7 cm.)

PROVENANCE:
The Downtown Gallery, New York.
Mr. and Mrs. Chapin Riley, Worcester, Massachusetts.

LITERATURE:
S. Reich, *John Marin: Catalogue Raisonné*, Part II, Tucson, Arizona,
1970, p. 807, no. 52.41, illustrated

Estimate: $25,000-35,000

•114

GEORGIA O'KEEFFE (1887-1986)

Red and Blue No. II

watercolor on paper

11⅞ x 8⅞in. (30.2 x 22.6cm.)

PROVENANCE:
Doris Bry, New York.
Private Collection, 1976.
Washburn Gallery, New York.
Acquired by the present owner from the above in 1988.

LITERATURE:
S.W. Peters, *Becoming O'Keeffe: The Early Years*, New York, 1991, pp. 245, 247, illustrated

RELATED WORKS:
Red and Blue No.II, watercolor on paper, 12 x 9 in. (30.5 x 22.9 cm.), Private Collection

In 1916 Georgia O'Keeffe made her professional debut with a series of black and white charcoal drawings that are some of the most pioneering examples of American Modernism. That same year O'Keeffe produced a group of watercolors composed of simple bold colors, such as *Red and Blue No. II* which represented a further investigation of pure abstraction. The small and seminal body of works on paper produced between 1915 and 1917 are some of the earliest and most original abstract images in the history of American art.

While teaching in Canyon, Texas, O'Keeffe in 1915 "[purged] the mannerisms acquired over her long tutelage" and decided, as she states, to "think things out for myself.. and draw the things in my head that are not like what anyone has taught—shapes and ideas so near to me— so natural to my way of being and thinking that it hasn't occurred to me to put hem down." (as quoted in C. C. Eldridge, *Georgia O'Keeffe*, New York, 1991, pp 20-21) *Red and Blue No.II* was borne from this transformation in O'Keeffe's art. Composed of brilliant and varying hues of red and blue, *Red and Blue No. II* is an early affirmation of O'Keeffe's passion for color. "O'Keeffe's early attraction to color developed through her love of the outdoors, a Midwestern upbringing, and her early art education in girls' schools. Colors meant more to her than words. Critic Henry McBride would point out that O'Keeffe's color "outblazed" that of the other painter in the Steiglitz circle." (J. G. Castro, *The Art and Life of Georgia O'Keeffe*, New York, 1985, p.162) O'Keeffe in a letter to her close friend Anita Pollitzer dated 11 September 1916, proclaims with great exuberance her love of the color and visual energy that surrounded her in Texas: "Tonight I walked into the sunset—to mail some letters—The whole sky—and there is much of it out here—was just blazing—and grey blue clouds were rioting all through the hotness of it—and the ugly little buildings and windmills looked great against it. But home-and kept on walking—The Eastern sky was all grey blue—bunches of clouds—different kinds of clouds—sticking around everywhere and the whole thing—lit up—first in one place —then in another with flashes of lightning—sometimes just sheet lightning—and sometimes sheet lightning with a sharp bright zigzag flashing across it...." (as quoted in J. Cowart, J. Hamilton, %Georgia O'Keeffe, Art and Letters, Washington, DC, 1988, pp. 156-157.

By 1915, according to Sarah Whitaker Peters, O'Keeffe "wanted her paintings to work like visual poems, to resist the intellect almost entirely. Hence her forms were simplified to their essence and her colors were orchestrated for physic resonance..." (*Becoming O'Keeffe, The Early Years*, New York, 1991, p. 13) Jack Cowart further comments: "O'Keeffe used color as emotion... Whether her images are abstract of figurative, O'Keeffe gives the viewer a profound lesson in emotional and intellectual coloring. No reproduction will ever do justice to the intensity, the solidity, or the high pitch of these colors, for the notion of local or topical color in her work is only relative, just the beginning point... .(%Georgia O'Keeffe , p.4.) Composed of amorphous forms of varying hues, *Red and Blue No. II* evokes the raw and personal emotion that found continious expression in her works though- out her career.

The National Gallery of Art and Georgia O'Keeffe Foundation, with this painting will be considered for inclusion in forthcoming *catalogue raisonné* of the artist's work, a joint project of the National Gallery of Art and Georgia O'Keeffe Foundation, with the assistance of the Burnett Foundation and the Henry Luce Foundation. Author: Barbara Buhler Lynes.

Estimate: $80,000-120,000

114

115

PROPERTY FROM THE ESTATE OF SHIRLEY POLYKOFF

•115

STUART DAVIS (1894-1964)

Nautical Shapes

signed with estate stamp 'Stuart Davis' (lower right)
ink on paper
22⅞ x 22⅝ in. (58.1 x 57.5 cm.)

EXHIBITED:
New York, Borgenicht Gallery, *Stuart Davis: Works on Paper*, January 1979, no. 20, illustrated
Summit, New Jersey, Summit Art Center, *Stuart Davis*, April–May 1979, no. 58
Houston, Texas, Museum of Fine Arts, *Stuart Davis: Drawings and Prints*, July–September 1979

This work will be included in the forthcoming *catalogue raisonné* of the artist's work.

Estimate: $30,000-50,000

116

PROPERTY FROM THE COLLECTION OF THE LATE BAYARD EWING

•116

JOHN STORRS (1885-1956)

Study in Pure Form (Forms in Space, No. 4)

inscribed with initials 'JS' and numbered 'I/X'

steel, copper and brass

14 in. (35.6 cm.) high, including black marble base

LITERATURE:

N. Frackman, *John Storrs*, New York, 1986, pp. 63-66, illustration of another example

Estimate: $25,000-35,000

167

•117

ARTHUR DOVE (1880-1946)

Dark Abstraction

oil on canvas

21⅜ x 18 in. (54.3 x 45.8 cm.)

PROVENANCE:
The Downtown Gallery, New York.
Terry Dinenfass Gallery, New York.
William S. Janss, Sun Valley, Idaho, 1979.
Terry Dintenfass Gallery, New York.
Acquired by the present owner from the above in 1980.

EXHIBITED:
Washington DC, Phillips Collection, *Arthur Dove and Duncan Phillips: Artist and Patron*, June-August 1981, no. 13 (This exhibition also traveled to Atlanta, Georgia, High Museum of Art, September-October 1981; Kansas City, Missouri, William Rockhill Nelson Gallery and Atkins Museum of Fine Arts, November 1981-January 1982; Houston, Texas, Museum of Fine Arts, January-March 1982; Columbus, Ohio, Columbus Museum of Art, April-June 1982; Seattle, Washington, Seattle Art Museum, July-September 1982; Milwaukee, Wisconsin, New Milwaukee Art Center, September-November 1982)

LITERATURE:
A.L. Morgan, *Arthur Dove, Life and Work, with a Catalogue Raisonné*, Newark, Delaware, 1984, pp. 49, 121-122, no. 20.2, illustrated

Dove throughout his career drew visual and spiritual inspiration from his immediate natural environment. From these surroundings, Dove abstracted natural forms into simple shapes, color and lines that became central motifs in his paintings. *Dark Abstraction* from *circa* 1920 reflects Doves unwavering fascination with the natural world coupled with his feverish investigations into abstraction, quintessential elements that made him renowned as one of the most important American modernist painters.

1920 was a turbulent year in Dove's private life. He and his wife Florence separated because of the financial hardship that resulted from Dove's desire to paint and remain close to nature on their farm in Westport, Connecticut. At the same time his relationship with Helen "Reds" Torr, another artist who was residing in Westport whom he had met the previous year, was beginning to flourish. Torr very much supported Dove and his artistic pursuits and they would remain together until the artist's death twenty-six years later. The family farm in Westport had demanded the majority of Dove's time and became a financial drain, limiting Dove's creative output. Dove's small body of works executed during this period somewhat reflected the artist's state of being, though according to A.L. Morgan, it is still difficult to arrange chronologically.

Dove worked primarily in charcoal between 1917 and 1921. These drawings represented further permutations of Dove's earlier artistic thinking illustrated in a series of abstract pastels executed in 1912-13. Barbara Haskell described the general characteristics of these works: "Forms coincided with color areas and were clearly defined by the use of dark perimeter lines....Dove called these lines the "character lines" of an object and spoke of their being determined by the meeting or intersection of planes of color. They, in effect followed the outer edges of planes and gave a sense of dimension to the forms." (*Arthur Dove*, Boston, Massachusetts, 1974, pp 21, 23)

The pronounced stylistic elements of these drawings, which were composed of heavy line and simple forms drawn from nature, influenced the oils produced in the early 1920s, such as *Dark Abstraction*. A. L. Morgan notes: "The almost non- referential charcoal drawings done during the hiatus in his painting may have served Dove as sources of ideas over a period of as much as three years. *Dark Abstraction*, which is closely based upon one of those drawings, seems to have been done after Dove's return to painting.....These drawings and the ensuing paintings are near to complete abstractions, but they are more structured than the very loose compositions of c. 1914/17. They all comprise large, handsome forms that insinuate only very limited three-dimensional space." (*Arthur Dove: Life and Work with a Catalogue Raisonné*, Newark, Delaware, 1984, p.49)

Dark Abstraction, which possibly refers to a work entitled *Woods* from 1920 in Dove's card file of paintings, reflects the artist's elemental reference to natural forms. Dove abstracts naturally spawned shapes into a series of bold intersecting lines and interlocking planes. The artist manipulates rich earthy browns and blacks to define the imposing geometric forms that dissect the surface of the work. Beneath these formidable shapes are interlocking planes comprised of varying tones of vegetal greens that pulsate with energy, creating a subtle yet constant tension between the two levels. *Dark Abstraction* poignantly illustrates at once Dove's uniquely bold forays into abstraction, and illustrates the form, color and line motifs that manifested in Dove's work throughout his life.

Estimate: $120,000-180,000

117

118

•118

CHARLES SHEELER (1883-1965)

Abstraction

signed and dated 'Sheeler 48' (lower right)
tempera on paper laid down on board
5⅜ x 7⅛ in. (13.2 x 18.1 cm.)

PROVENANCE:
The Downtown Gallery, New York
Terry Dintenfass Gallery, New York

Estimate: $15,000-25,000

119

•119

HUGH HENRY BRECKENRIDGE (1870-1937)

Genesis: The Birth of Light

signed 'Hugh H. Breckenridge' (lower left)—signed again
and inscribed with title on a label attached to the reverse
oil on canvas
37 x 43 in. (94 x 109.2 cm.)

EXHIBITED:
Philadelphia, Pennsylvania, Pennsylvania Academy of the Fine
Arts, *One Hundred and Twenty-Fifth Annual Exhibition*, January-
March 1930, no. 298, illustrated.

Estimate: $30,000-50,000

•120

MILTON AVERY (1885-1965)
Basket of Fish
signed 'Milton Avery' (lower left)
oil on canvas
32 x 48 in. (81.3 x 121.9 cm.)

PROVENANCE:
Estate of Wilfred P. Cohen, New York.
Pace Wildenstein, New York.
Acquired by the present owner from the above.

EXHIBITED:
Washington, DC, National Collection of Fine Arts, Smithsonian
Institution, *Milton Avery*, December 1969-January 1970 no. 14,
illustrated (This exhibition also traveled to: Brooklyn, New York,
The Brooklyn Museum, February-March 1970; Columbus, Ohio,
The Columbus Gallery of Fine Arts, April-May 1970), no. 14,
illustrated
New York, Whitney Museum of American Art, *Milton Avery*,
September-December 1982, no. 151 (This exhibition also traveled
to Pittsburgh, Pennsylvania, Museum of Art, Carnegie Institute,
January-March 1983; Fort Worth, Texas, Fort Worth Art
Museum, March-May 1983; Buffalo, New York, Albright-Knox
Art Gallery, May-July 1983; Denver, Colorado, The Denver Art
Museum, July-September 1983; Minneapolis, Minnesota, Walker
Art Center, September-October 1983)

LITERATURE:
H. Kramer, *Milton Avery: Paintings 1930-1960*, New York, 1962,
no. 81, illustrated

This painting will be included in Dr. Marla Price's forthcoming
catalogue raisonné of the works of Milton Avery.

Estimate: $120,000-180,000

120

121

PROPERTY OF MR. AND MRS. GEORGE BERMAN

•121

MILTON AVERY (1885-1965)

Little Girl in Forest

signed and dated 'Milton Avery 1943' (lower right)—signed
and dated again and inscribed with title on the reverse
watercolor on paper
22 x 30 in. (55.9 x 76.2 cm.)

PROVENANCE:
Makler Gallery, Philadelphia, Pennsylvania.
Acquired by the present owner from the above, 1968.

Estimate: $25,000-35,000

122

VARIOUS PROPERTIES

•122
MARSDEN HARTLEY (1877-1943)
Rope, Seashells and Starfish
oil on canvasboard
12 x 16 in. (30.5 x 40.6 cm.)

PROVENANCE:
William Macbeth, Inc., New York.

Estimate: $60,000–80,000

123

•123

WOLF KAHN (b. 1927)
At the Foot of the Blue Hills
signed 'W Kahn' (lower right)—inscribed with title on the
stretcher
oil on canvas
36 x 52 in. (91.5 x 132.1 cm.)

Estimate: $15,000–20,000

124

PROPERTY OF MR. AND MRS. GEORGE BERMAN

•124

MILTON AVERY (1885-1965)

Rose and Blue Teapot

signed and dated 'Milton Avery 1949' (lower right)—signed
and dated again and inscribed with title on the reverse
oil on canvasboard
14 x 18in. (35.6 x 45.7cm.)

PROVENANCE:
Estate of the artist.
Makler Gallery, Philadelphia, Pennsylvania.
Acquired by the present owner from the above in 1971.

EXHIBITED:
Philadelphia, Pennsylvania, Makler Gallery, *Avery: Oils, Watercolors
and Graphics*, November 1966
Philadelphia, Pennsylvania, Makler Gallery, *Milton Avery: Oils,
Watercolors and Graphics*, December 1968

LITERATURE:
B. Haskell, *Milton Avery*, New York, no. 92, pp. 113, 116,
illustrated

This painting will be included in Dr. Marla Price's forthcoming
catalogue raisonné of the works of Milton Avery.

Estimate: $20,000-30,000

125

•125

EDWIN WALTER DICKINSON (1891-1978)
Screen Door
signed 'E. Dickinson' on the reverse
oil on canvas
24 x 23¾ in. (61 x 60.3 cm.)

PROVENANCE:
The artist.
Private collection, New York, *circa* 1960.
By descent in the family to the present owner.

EXHIBITED:
Washington, DC, Hirschhorn Museum and Sculpture Garden, Smithsonian Institution, *Edwin Dickinson: Selected Landscapes*, September-December 1980, no. 1, illustrated (This exhibition also traveled to Louisville, Kentucky, J.B. Speed Art Museum, January-March 1981)

Estimate: $20,000-30,000

126

PROPERTY FROM THE COLLECTION OF THE LATE BAYARD EWING

•126

WALTER TANDY MURCH (1907-1967)

Air Filter

signed, dated '1966' and inscribed with title on the reverse
oil on canvas
50 x 36 in. (127 x 91.5 cm.)

EXHIBITED:
Brooklyn, New York, The Brooklyn Museum of Art, *Walter Murch Retrospective*, December 1967-January 1968,
no. 112

Estimate: $30,000-50,000

•127

NORMAN ROCKWELL (1894-1978)

The Runaway

signed 'Norman Rockwell' (lower right)

oil on canvas

36 x 24 in. (91.5 x 61 cm.)

PROVENANCE:
Judy Goffman Fine Art, New York.
Acquired by the present owner from the above in 1970.

LITERATURE:
Life Magazine, June 1, 1922, cover illustration
L.N. Moffatt, *Norman Rockwell: A Definitive Catalogue*, Stockbridge, Massachusetts, 1986, p. 45, no. C119, illustrated

Norman Rockwell's poignant representations of America's youth are a beloved record of American life throughout the early and middle twentieth century. His renown is based upon the illustrations that he produced from the early 1910s through the 1970s for America's leading magazines. More than illustrations, he left behind an historical artistic legacy that is unmatched by any other American artist.

Indeed, both art connoisseurs and historians look to Rockwell's work as a barometer of American culture. The scope of his appeal is still expanding as generations grow up and experience the same episodes that Rockwell painted for several decades. "For six decades, through two World Wars, the Great Depression, unprecedented national prosperity and radical social change, Norman Rockwell held up a mirror to America and reflected its identity through the portraits he painted of its people. Rockwell painted real people—freckles, wrinkles, big ears and all—and, like an art director, he staged entire scenes, creating settings and suggesting situations for them. His work, as reproduced on millions of magazine covers, proved to be arresting on the newsstands, and established a distinctive look for the Saturday Evening Post that was a major factor in its popularity. But Rockwell's paintings have done more than just sell magazines. They are in a large measure the visual memory of a nation." (V. Crenson, *Norman Rockwell's Portrait of America*, New York, 1989, p. 9)

Typical of Rockwell's spirited illustrations, *The Runaway* tells a story that is instantaneously obvious to every viewer. By including numerous details, he gives the story potential elaborations on the central theme that can be invented by each individual. One immediately gleans that this painting tells the story of every young boys's dream to run away from home and join the circus. Predictably, however, during his travels, no matter how long or short, he has realized how much his family means to him, and how much he misses the home that he has recently abandoned. As he breaks down, a kindly circus clown and his dog take the time to comfort him. Based on the clown's knowing look, the viewer is at once comforted in the fact that the boy has learned a lesson and that he will soon return home safely. At the same time, one is amused at the lofty aspirations and resilience of such a young boy. Central to Rockwell's body of work are themes that endure, the most important of which is the notion of the family. It is at the core of almost all of his works, and the present work is no exception. The young boy has discovered that despite the alluring excitement of the circus, his family is far more important to him, one of the most important lessons that one can learn during their lifetime.

A close analysis of Rockwell's preferred themes proves that the features of *The Runaway* are some of his most successful. "Situations involving small embarrassments, discomforts, and humiliation have provided humorous covers all the way through. Growing up is another and, closely related, is budding love. Old-fashioned patriotism persists as well as the recording of fads and historical events. Youth contrasted with age is a major category, recurring almost as often as depictions of simple joys for the vicarious delight of the reader. More specific long-term subject matter introduced in this first decade includes, in order of appearance, Santa Claus, Boy Scouts, circus people, dogs and bandaged big toes." (T.S. Buechner, *Norman Rockwell: A Sixty Year Retrospective*, New York, 1972, pp. 44-45) Running away from home to join the circus could be considered under a number of categories from small embarrassments to growing up.

This work appeared on the cover of *LIFE* Magazine in 1922. Today, *LIFE* is still one of America's most beloved periodicals, but at the time, "*LIFE* magazine ranked second to the *Post* in popularity around 1920 ... Ranking high in popularity ... the *LIFE* covers appeared regularly until 1924." (L.N. Moffatt, *Norman Rockwell: A Definitive Catalogue*, Stockbridge, Massachusetts, 1986. p. 37) Being published on the cover of a prestigious magazine no doubt helped Rockwell's early career, but more important to the artist was the dissemination of a moral that was dear to his heart.

An original copy of the cover of *Life Magazine* of June 1, 1922 accompanies the lot.

Estimate: $500,000-700,000

127

128

VARIOUS PROPERTIES

•128

OGDEN PLEISSNER (1905-1983) Check
The Shore Line — Cotton Bay, Bahamas
signed 'Pleissner' (lower right)
oil on canvas
20 x 34 in. (50.8 x 86.3cm.)

Estimate: $20,000-30,000

129

•129

STEPHEN SCOTT YOUNG (b. 1957)

Spider

signed and dated 'S S Young 1987' (lower right)—signed
again, dated 'November 1987' and inscribed with title and
various notations on the reverse

watercolor on paper

22½ x 30 in. (57.1 x 76.2 cm.)

Estimate: $25,000–35,000

130

•130

STEPHEN SCOTT YOUNG (b. 1957)
Junkanoo
signed 'S S Young' (lower left)
watercolor on paper
28¾ x 30 in. (73 x 76.2 cm.)

Estimate: $40,000-60,000

131

•131

STEPHEN SCOTT YOUNG (b. 1957)

Church on the Common, Townshend Vermont

signed and dated 'SS Young 88' (upper right)—signed again,
dated 'Summer 87-88' and inscribed with title and various
notations on the reverse

watercolor and pencil on paper

24¾ x 22 in. (62.8 x 55.8 cm.)

PROVENANCE:
Acquired by the present owner from the artist, 1989.

Estimate: $20,000-30,000

END OF SALE

INDEX

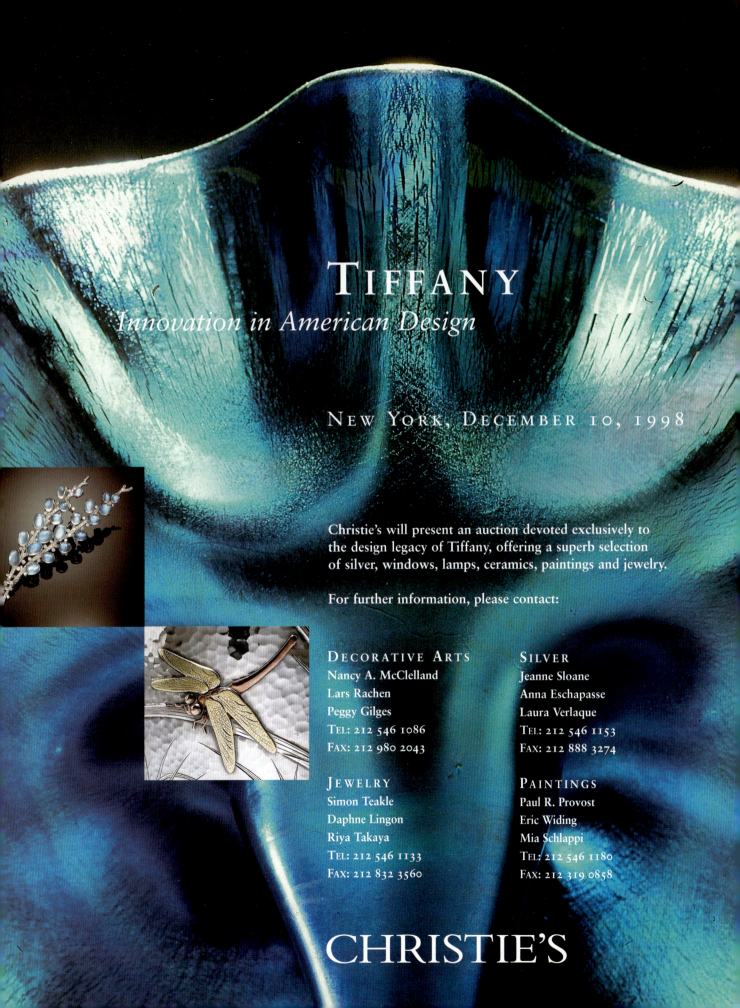

The Chieffo Collection
including American Portrait Miniatures

Attributed to Joseph Whiting Stock (1815–1855)
Portrait Miniature of Baby J. M. Hardy

New York, 19 January 1999
Important American Furniture, Silver, Prints, Folk Art and Decorative Arts

ENQUIRIES: (212) 546 1181

VENUE: Christie's, 502 Park Avenue, New York, N.Y. 10022 Tel: (212) 546 1000

CATALOGUES: London on (44171) 389 2820
or New York on (800) 395 6300

CHRISTIE'S

Internet: http://www.christies.com

The Collection of
Mr. and Mrs. James L. Britton

New York, 16 and 19 January 1999

ENQUIRIES: (212) 546 1182

VENUE: Christie's, 502 Park Avenue, New York, N.Y. 10022 Tel: (212) 546 1000

CATALOGUES: London on (44171) 389 2820
or New York on (800) 395 6300

CHRISTIE'S

Internet: http://www.christies.com

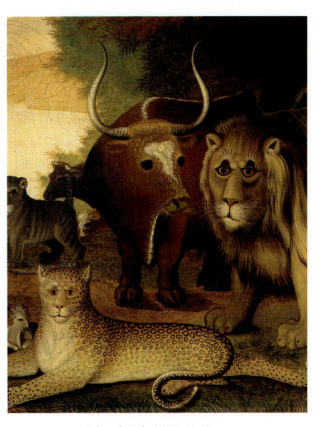

Absentee Bid Form

Client #_____

CHRISTIE'S

502 Park Avenue, New York, New York 10022

_____
billing name (please print)

_____
address

_____
city   state   zip code

_____
daytime telephone

_____
evening telephone   fax #

_____
signature

_____
sale title and code   sale date

SALE TITLE   Important American Paintings, Drawings and Sculpture

DATE   Wednesday 2 December 1998 at 10 a.m.

CODE NAME   PARK

SALE NO.   9006

[Dealers: Billing name and address should agree with your state or local sales tax exemption certificate. Invoices cannot be changed after they have been printed.]

I request that Christie's enter bids on the following lots up to the maximum price I have indicated for each lot.

I understand that if my bid is successful, the purchase price will be the sum of my final bid plus a premium of 15% of the final bid price up to and including $50,000 and 10% of the amount above $50,000 ("buyer's premium") and any applicable state or local sales or use tax.

I understand that Christie's executes absentee bids as a convenience for clients and is not responsible for inadvertently failing to execute bids or for errors relating to execution of bids. On my behalf, Christie's will try to purchase these lots for the lowest possible price, taking into account the reserve and other bids.

If identical absentee bids are left, Christie's will give precedence to the first one received. All successful bids are subject to the terms of the Limited Warranty. Absence of Other Warranties and Conditions of Sale printed in the front of each Christie's catalogue.

Lot Number (in numerical order)	Bid $ (excluding buyer's premium)	Lot Number (in numerical order)	Bid $ (excluding buyer's premium)	Lot Number (in numerical order)	Bid $ (excluding buyer's premium)

To be sure that bids will be accepted and delivery of lots not delayed, bidders not yet known to Christie's should supply a bank reference.

_____
name of bank(s)

_____
address of bank(s)

_____
accounts number(s)

_____
name of account officer(s)

_____
bank telephone number

To allow time for processing, absentee bids should be received at least 24 hours before the sale begins. Christie's will confirm all bids received by fax by return fax. If you have not received our confirmation within one business day, please resubmit your bid(s) or contact the Bid Department at telephone (212) 546 1129 or fax (212) 832 2216.

CHRISTIE'S SERVICES

In addition to holding regular international art auctions in over 80 categories, Christie's offers a variety of professional art-related services. More information on these services, listed below, can be obtained as indicated.

Appraisal Services

Accurate and up-to-date appraisals are an essential part of collecting. Christie's prepares authoritative appraisals for insurance, estate tax or family division purposes, fair market value assessment or charitable contributions. Christie's standard appraisal fees are very competitive and can often cost less than a local market appraisal. Additionally, if appraised property is consigned to Christie's within one year of the appraisal, all or a pro rated part of the fees will be rebated. For further details, please contact Marc Porter at (212) 546 1008.

Trust and Estate Services

Christie's offers lawyers, bankers, financial planners, trust officers and families a complete range of services tailored specifically to their needs. These include the successful disposition of estate property at auction and the preparation of appraisals of tangible personal property. Our professional staff around the country works one-on-one with advisors on matters involving either a single item or an entire collection. Specific questions on such services may be directed to Amy Corcoran at (212) 546 5819.

Financial Services

Christie's is able to offer clients financial assistance regarding consignments. On occasion, for example, Christie's advances funds to vendors against property consigned for sale. For further details on these services, please contact Ray Horne at (212) 702 1392.

Education

Christie's New York Art Course offers an outstanding opportunity to explore the development of 19th and 20th Century art. Distinguished art historians, critics and writers present a regular series of lectures, supplemented by guided visits to museums, artists' studios, current exhibitions, galleries, private collections and Christie's salerooms. Participants acquire a sound art history background combined with opportunities to develop a good eye and connoisseurship through first-hand contact with works of art. Weekend visits to Boston, Philadelphia and Washington are also organized.

The course consists of three nine-week terms. Lectures are held three mornings a week, Tuesday through Thursday. Terms are structured as follows:
Fall Term – Romanticism to Post-Impressionism, Winter Term – Fauvism to Surrealism, and Spring Term – Abstract Expressionism to the Present Day.

Applicants may enroll for any or all terms of the three-term, year-long program. Enrollment is limited. For application forms or further information, contact Sandra Joys, Director, Christie's New York Art Course, 502 Park Avenue, New York, New York 10022, Tel: (212) 546 1092, Fax: (212) 446 9566.

Catalogue Subscriptions and Publications

Each year Christie's publishes more than 1,200 different catalogues, covering more than 80 categories sold throughout our salerooms worldwide. These catalogues are fully illustrated and researched, and together with other publications, can be purchased individually or by subscription at a considerable saving. For further information, contact Christie's Publications, 21-24 44th Avenue, Long Island City, New York 11101, Tel: (800) 395 6300 or (718) 784 1480; Fax: (800) 395 5600 or (718) 786 0941. If not resident in the Americas, contact Christie's Publications in the United Kingdom at Tel: (4471) 389 2820 or Fax: (4471) 389 2869.

Security Storage

Christie's offers state-of-the-art security storage facilities in London to clients from all over the world. This centrally located purpose-built warehouse is environmentally controlled and can accommodate individual works or entire collections. For further information please call Sydney Gill in London at (4471) 622 0609.

COLLECTION AND HANDLING CHARGES

IMPORTANT INFORMATION FOR BUYERS

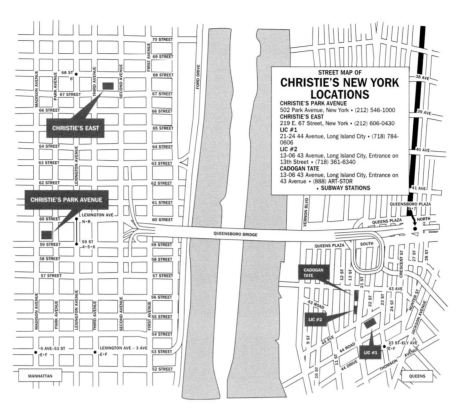

Location of New York salerooms and warehouses

All lots purchased in this sale will be held free of charge for 28 days from the sale date.★

After the sale, certain purchased lots will be held at Cadogan Tate Fine Art Storage Limited at 13-06 43rd Avenue, Long Island City, NY 11101, tel: (888) 278 7887, fax: (718) 361 5705.

Handling charges will be payable on all lots still held at Cadogan Tate after 28 days from the sale.

While at Christie's or Cadogan Tate, lots are available for collection on any weekday, 9:00am to 4:30 pm.
Lots may not be collected during the day of their move to Cadogan Tate.

CHARGES

Lots collected from Christie's or Cadogan Tate within 28 days of the auction are free of charges.
Charges per lot for purchases collected from Cadogan Tate are:

	Paintings/Small Objects	Furniture/Large Objects
Administration:	$30.00	$60.00
Storage per day:	$3.00	$6.00

These charges are subject to New York State Sales Tax and an insurance surcharge.

★This program does not apply to property over $250,000 in value. Not all property is eligible for the Cadogan Tate program. **Please consult the Pick-Up Information Sheet for specific collection information on the lots in this sale.**

The Pick-Up Information Sheet may be updated and obtained from the Bidder Registration staff, Packing Desk, Cashiers or Customer Service staff.

NY 23/4/97

CATALOGUE SUBSCRIPTIONS ORDER FORM

CHRISTIE'S CATALOGUES

Christie's catalogues are a vital source of information, beautifully produced and richly illustrated, with every lot described in detail by expert specialists and often accompanied by fascinating historical and other notes.

A subscription ensures that the catalogues are sent to you automatically as soon as available, giving you time to read them at leisure before viewing.

Subscribers are sent price lists after each sale, keeping them up-to-date with prices and market trends and many collectors, dealers and institutions find the catalogues invaluable for reference long after the auction.

I should like to receive the catalogues I have indicated:

AMERICAN PAINTINGS

SALE LOCATION:	CATEGORY CODE	APPROX. NO. OF SALES	THE AMERICAS	REST OF EUROPE	OUTSIDE EUROPE	UNITED KINGDOM
☐ NEW YORK, PARK AVENUE includes one sale in Los Angeles.	N14	4	$120	£80	£85	£75
☐ NEW YORK, CHRISTIE'S EAST	E14	2	$50	£36	£40	£33
☐ ALL CATALOGUES ABOVE — 15% DISCOUNT	Y14	6	$145	£99	£106	£92

N B Price varies according to delivery address

PLEASE RETURN TO:

Christie's Catalogues
21-24 44th Avenue, Long Island City
New York 11101, USA

USA & Canada
Tel. 800 395 6300
Fax 800 395 5600

Americas outside USA & Canada
Tel. +718 784 1480
Fax +718 786 0941

UK
Christie's Catalogues
21-25 South Lambeth Road,
London SW8 1SX, UK
Tel. 0171 389 2820
Fax 0171 389 2869

Outside UK
Tel. +44 171 389 2820
Fax +44 171 389 2869

Residents of AL, CA, CT, DC, FL, IL, MA, NJ, NY, PA, RI, TX please add your local sales tax.

Method of payment:

☐ Visa   ☐ MasterCard   ☐ American Express

Card No. _____

Expiry Date _____

Card Member Signature _____

☐ US/UK check in $/£ (payable to Christie's)

☐ Eurocheque in GB £ (payable to Christie's)

Send catalogue(s) to:

Name _____

Address _____

_____

_____

Daytime Tel. _____

Fax: _____

CHRISTIE'S CHARGES

Buyers

Christie's charges a premium to the buyer on the final bid price of each lot sold at the following rates:
15% of the final bid price up to and including $50,000 and 10% of the final bid price above $50,000.

Consignors

All consignors—whether private, trade or institutional—pay a commission according to a fixed scale of charges based upon the value of property sold at auction in a calendar year at Christie's salerooms worldwide.

If a consignor has sold property through Christie's during the prior calendar year, the commission rate payable will be the lesser of (i) the commission rate payable under the scale of charges outlined below or (ii) the amount that the consignor would have paid during the prior calendar year under this commission structure.

Private Consignors

If annual sales total less than $100,000, a commission is charged on each lot sold at its final bid price at the following rates:

less than $2,000	20% of the final bid price
$2,000 — $7,499	15% of the final bid price
$7,500 — $99,999	10% of the final bid price

If annual sales equal or exceed $100,000, the commission rate payable is based on the aggregate value of all consigned property at the following rates:

$100,000 — $249,999	9% of the final bid price
$250,000 — $499,999	8% of the final bid price
$500,000 — $999,999	6% of the final bid price
$1,000,000 — $2,499,999	5% of the final bid price
$2,500,000 — $4,999,999	4% of the final bid price
$5,000,000 or more	2% of the final bid price

Trade Consignors

If annual sales total less than $100,000, a commission is charged on each lot sold at its final bid price at the following rates:

less than $2,000	15% of the final bid price
$2,000 — $7,499	10% of the final bid price
$7,500 — $99,999	6% of the final bid price

If annual sales equal or exceed $100,000, the commission rate payable is based on the aggregate value of all consigned property at the following rates:

$100,000 — $999,999	6% of the final bid price
$1,000,000 — $2,499,999	5% of the final bid price
$2,500,000 — $4,999,999	4% of the final bid price
$5,000,000 or more	2% of the final bid price

Institutional Consignors

If annual sales total less than $100,000, a commission is charged on each lot sold at its final bid price at the following rates:

less than $2,000	15% of the final bid price
$2,000 — $7,499	10% of the final bid price
$7,500 — $99,999	5% of the final bid price

If annual sales equal or exceed $100,000, the commission rate payable is based on the aggregate value of all consigned property at the following rates:

$100,000 — $999,999	5% of the final bid price
$1,000,000 — $2,499,999	3% of the final bid price
$2,500,000 or more	2% of the final bid price

Stamps and Wine

Consignors of stamps selling for less than $100,000 in a year pay a different commission from that outlined above:

less than $2,000	15% of the final bid price
$2,000 — $99,999	10% of the final bid price

Consignors of wine selling for less than $100,000 also pay a different commission:

less than $7,500	15% of the final bid price
$7,500 — $99,999	10% of the final bid price

Coins and Bank Notes

Coins, bank notes and commemorative medals are sold by Spink America Inc., an affiliated company. Prospective consignors should contact Spink America directly at 212 546 1056 for further information on its charges.

1/10/97

Minimum Commission

There is a minimum commission charge for all lots sold except for stamps.

The minimum charge for all property other than wine is $100 for each lot sold at our Park Avenue galleries and $50 for each lot sold at Christie's East. The minimum commission charge for wine is $30 for each lot sold.

Unsold Lots

A charge of 5% of the reserve may be made on each lot failing to reach its reserve.

Other Charges

Where applicable, there will be charges for insurance, illustration, restoration, freight and transit insurance.

Administration, Handling and Insurance Charges

For 28 calendar days after the auction, uncollected purchases are held at our gallery or warehouse premises free of charge. Thereafter, uncollected purchases will incur handling, administration and insurance charges, which will be managed by Cadogan Tate on behalf of Christie's, at the rates specified below.

Unsold lots which are not collected by 35 days after the auction will also incur handling, administration and insurance charges at the following rates:

Paintings and Small Objects:
Administration: $30.00
Handling per day: $3.00

Furniture and Large Objects:
Administration: $60.00
Handling per day: $6.00

All lots:
Insurance: Lower of 0.5% of insured value/total of above charges.

New York State Sales Tax: 8.25% of above charges.

Note to all buyers:

Buyers are reminded of their responsibility for purchased lots as outlined in paragraphs 7 and 8 of our Conditions of Sale, printed in the front of this catalogue. **At the fall of the auctioneer's hammer, the buyer assumes full responsibility for the lot.**

Beginning on the 29th day after the auction, all lots are insured at the purchase price, including the buyer's premium. In the event of any damage, Christie's will be liable at our sole option only for the cost of repairing or restoring the property.

Lots may only be collected with the approval of the Purchase Payments office at Christie's, which will be given only when all amounts due Christie's and Cadogan Tate, as agent of Christie's, have been paid in full. Charges may be paid in advance or at the time of collection by cash, cheque, wire transfer, credit card, bank draft, or traveller's cheque. Please call 888-278-7887 to ascertain the amount due.

Charges at Other Salerooms

Commission and other charges may vary slightly at our other salerooms.

SALES TAX

Buyers

Buyers are required to pay any sales or use tax which may be due, unless exempt by law. Purchases picked up at Christie's or Christie's East or delivered to any location in New York, Alabama, California, Connecticut, Florida, Illinois, Massachusetts, New Jersey, Pennsylvania, Rhode Island, Texas or Washington, D.C. are subject to sales or compensating use tax of such jurisdiction, unless the buyer is exempted by law.

Consignors

As agent for the consignor, Christie's is responsible for the collection and remittance of sales or use tax from the buyer.

NY 6/7/98

CHRISTIE'S DEPARTMENTS

SPECIALIST DEPARTMENTS

Director of Specialist Departments
Christopher Hartop (212) 546 1019

American Furniture & Decorative Arts
Tel: (212) 546 1181
Fax: (212) 223 3985
John Hays
Martha Willoughby
Jennifer Olshin
Susan D. Kleckner, *American Folk Art*

Dean F. Failey, *Senior Director*
(212) 702 5489

American Indian Art and Western Memorabilia
Tel: (212) 606 0536
Fax: (212) 517 8411
Elyse Luray Marx
Hadley Colburn Freeman
Stacy Marcus Chidekel, *Consultant*
Allen Wardwell, *Consultant*

American Paintings
Tel: (212) 546 1179
Fax: (212) 319 0858
Andrew Schoelkopf
Paul R. Provost
Eric Widing
Mia A. Schläppi
  Los Angeles
    Tel: (310) 385 2655
    Fax: (310) 385 0246

Antiquities
Tel: (212) 546 1075
Fax: (212) 446 9569
G. Max Bernheimer
Molly Morse

Art Nouveau, Art Deco, Arts & Crafts
Tel: (212) 546 1084
Fax: (212) 980 2043
Lars Rachen
Peggy Gilges

Nancy A. McClelland
Senior Director

Books & Manuscripts
Tel: (212) 546 1195
Fax: (212) 980 2043
Francis Wahlgren
Chris Coover, *Manuscripts*
Anne Tozzi
Nina Musinsky, *Consultant*
Bart Auerbach, *Consultant*
Hope Mayo, *Consultant*
Stephen C. Massey,
Senior International Consultant

Felix de Marez Oyens
Director, International Department
(212) 546 1197

Chinese Ceramics & Works of Art
Tel: (212) 546 1160
Fax: (212) 888 7025
Athena Zonars
Sarah Wong
Patricia Curtin, *Consultant*
  Los Angeles
    Tel: (310) 385 0613
    Fax: (310) 385 0246
    Michael Hughes
    (212) 546 1038
Theow-Huang Tow,
International Director

Chinese Paintings
Tel: (212) 546 1157
Fax: (212) 888 7025
Cheng-Ming Ma
Laura Whitman

Coins & Bank Notes (at Spink America)
Tel: (212) 546 1056
Fax: (212) 750 5874

Contemporary Art
Tel: (212) 546 1168
Fax: (212) 319 0858
Andrew Massad

Martha Baer, *Senior Director*
(212) 546 1144
Laura Paulson, *Senior Specialist*
  Los Angeles
    Tel: (310) 385 2660
    Fax: (310) 385 0246
    Deborah McLeod
    Robert Looker

European Ceramics & Glass
Tel: (212) 546 5821
Fax: (212) 223 3985
Jody Wilkie
Becky MacGuire, *Chinese Export*
Ellen Jenkins, *Consultant*
Lynne Stair, *Consultant*

European Furniture
Tel: (212) 546 1151
Fax: (212) 223 3985
Alistair Clarke
Melissa Gagen, *English Furniture*
Orlando Rock
Will Strafford, *French Furniture*
Natasha Schlesinger
Jessica Segal
Angus Wilkie, *Consultant*
John Hardy, *International Consultant*

  Los Angeles
    Tel: (310) 385 2678
    Fax: (310) 385 9295
    Andrea Fiuczynski

European Works of Art & Tapestries
Tel: (212) 546 1148
Fax: (212) 223 3985
Frances McCord Krongard
Andrew Butterfield

Impressionist and Nineteenth Century Art
Tel: (212) 546 1173
Fax: (212) 888 6485
Franck Giraud
Nicholas Maclean
Cyanne Chutkow
John Steinert, *Drawings and Watercolors*
Pamela Bingham
Andrew Butterfield
Constantine Frangos
Christine Grounds
Meredith Harper-Wiley,
Drawings & Works on Paper
Andrew Rose, *Sporting Paintings*

Michael Findlay, *International Director*
Polly Sartori, *Senior Director*

Indian and Southeast Asian Art
Tel: (212) 702 2666
Fax: (212) 750 1522
Hugo Weihe

Japanese Art
Tel: (212) 546 1156
Fax: (212) 888 7025
Yoshinori Munemura
Susan Lewis
Julia Meech, *Consultant*
Jane Oliver, *Consultant*

Jewelry
Tel: (212) 546 1133
Fax: (212) 832 3560
Simon Teakle
Daphne Lingon
Riya Takaya
  Boston
    Tel: (617) 536 6000
    Fax: (617) 536 0002
    Susan Florence
  Chicago
    Tel: (312) 787 2765
    Fax: (312) 951 7449
    Susan Florence
  Florida
    Tel: (561) 833 6952
    Fax: (561) 833 0007
    Susan Florence
  Los Angeles
    Tel: (310) 385 2666
    Fax: (310) 385 9295
    Glenn Spiro
    Brett O'Connor

Korean Art
Tel: (212) 546 1156
Fax: (212) 888 0927
Yoshinori Munemura
Heakyum Kim

Latin American Paintings
Tel: (212) 546 1099
Fax: (212) 888 0927
Fernando Gutierrez

NY 19/10/98

CHRISTIE'S DEPARTMENTS

Motor Cars
Tel: (310) 385 2699
Fax: (310) 385 0246
David Gooding
Miles Morris

Musical Instruments
Tel: (212) 702 2683
Fax: (212) 980 2043
Jonathan Stone

Nineteenth Century Furniture
Tel: (212) 606 0529
Fax: (212) 717 4725
Antonia M. Phillips

Old Master Paintings & Drawings
Tel: (212) 546 1178
Fax: (212) 319 0858
Anthony Crichton-Stuart
Sarah Lidsey
James Bruce-Gardyne
Alan Wintermute
Ilaria Quadrani, *Old Master Drawings*

Photographs
Tel: (212) 546 1063
Fax: (212) 980 2043
Rick Wester
Ellen de Boer
Leila Buckjune

Popular Arts
Tel: (212) 606 0543
Fax: (212) 517 8411
Simeon Lipman

Prints
Tel: (212) 546 1022
Fax: (212) 980 2043
Jonathan Rendell
Anne Spink
Christopher Gaillard
Kelly Troester

Rugs & Carpets
Tel: (212) 546 1187
Fax: (212) 223 3985
Elisabeth Poole

Russian Works of Art
Tel: (212) 702 2683
Fax: (212) 980 2043
Alexis de Tiesenhausen
Genevieve Wheeler

Silver and Objects of Vertu
Tel: (212) 546 1153
Fax: (212) 223 3985
Jeanne Sloane
Anna Eschapasse
Laura Verlaque

Christopher Hartop

Stamps
(at Spink America)
Tel: (212) 546 1087
Fax: (212) 750 5874
Brian Bleckwenn

Twentieth Century Art
Tel: (212) 546 1170
Fax: (212) 371 7261
Franck Giraud
Christopher Eykyn
Alison Buscher
John Steinert, *Drawings and Watercolors*
Richard Francis
Andrew Butterfield
Meredith Harper-Wiley, *Drawings & Works on Paper*
Mary Peck

Michael Findlay, *International Director*
Martha Baer, *Senior Director*
Laura Paulson, *Senior Specialist*
   Los Angeles
   Tel: (310) 385 2660
   Fax: (310) 385 0246
   Deborah McLeod
   Robert Looker

Watches
Tel: (212) 546 1012
Fax: (212) 832 3560
Doug Escribano
Ruth Zandberg

Wine
Tel: (212) 546 5830
Fax: (212) 317 2470
Christopher Burr
Jamie Wolff
Frederic C. Hatton, *Consultant*
   Los Angeles
   Tel: (310) 385 2600
   Fax: (310) 385 9292
   Cameron Hobel

CLIENT ADVISORY SERVICES
Tel: (212) 546 1036
Fax: (212) 750 1537

Kate Gubelmann
Kathy Kermian
Heidi Kucker
Kim Solow
Jennifer Kaplan
Sharon Kim
Gabriela Lobo
Elizabeth Sarnoff
Maria Los
Mirja Spooner

Mary Libby
Bonnie Stern
Angus Wilkie

Estates & Appraisals
Tel: (212) 546 1060
Fax: (212) 750 6498
Marc B. Porter
Amy Corcoran, *Attorney/Banker Services*
Linda Izzo, *Appraisals*
Deborah Ahearn, *Fine Arts Appraisals*
Thomas Root, *Decorative Arts Appraisals*
Stephen S. Lash
   Los Angeles
   Tel: (310) 385 2611
   Fax: (310) 385 9292
   Brooke Glassman Kanter

Financial Services
Tel: (212) 702 1392
Fax: (212) 754 2390
Ray Horne
Patricia G. Hambrecht

Internet Access
http://www.christies.com

Museum & Corporate Services
Tel: (212) 546 1190
Fax: (212) 446 9569
Allison Whiting

ADMINISTRATIVE DEPARTMENTS

General Counsel
Tel: (212) 546 1193
Fax: (212) 223 7289
Jo Backer Laird

Human Resources
Tel: (212) 546 1106
Fax: (212) 421 8722
Cindy Weiss Drankoski

Marketing & Public Relations
Tel: (212) 546 1146
Fax: (212) 421 8722
Susan Korb
Taggarty Patrick

Special Events
Tel: (212) 546 1007
Fax: (212) 446 9566

AUCTIONEERS
Susan Abeles (#924040)
Noël Annesley (#0950782)
James Bruce-Gardyne (#0940126)
Christopher Burge (#761543)
François Curiel (#761369)
Catherine D. Elkies (#866011)
Dean Failey (#799256)
Andrea Fiuczynski (#849132)
Christopher Hartop (#779124)
John Hays (#822982)
Ursula Hermacinski (#917819)
Sarah Lidsey (#0953093)
Nicholas Maclean (#925516)
Stephen C. Massey (#768546)
Patrick S. Meade (#866012)
Barbara Strongin (#849133)
Simon Teakle (#867918)
Francis Wahlgren (#868229)

SALEROOMS AND REPRESENTATIVES

North America and South America

Salerooms

Christie's Inc.
502 Park Avenue
New York, New York 10022
Tel: (212) 546 1000
Fax: (212) 980 8163
Christopher Burge, *Chairman*
Stephen S. Lash, *Vice Chairman*
Patricia G. Hambrecht, *President*
Geoffrey Iddison, *Chief Operating Officer*
Christopher Hartop, *Executive Vice President*

Christie's East
219 East 67th Street
New York, New York 10021
Tel: (212) 606 0400
Fax: (212) 737 6076
Catherine D. Elkies, *President*

Christie's Los Angeles
Marcia Wilson Hobbs, *Chairman*
Jean-René Saillard, *Managing Director*
Andrea Fiuczynski, *Director of Business Development*
360 North Camden Drive
Beverly Hills, California 90210
Tel: (310) 385 2600
Fax: (310) 385 9292
Christie's Education
Tel: (310) 385 2697
Fax: (310) 385 9327

Other Services

Christie's Education
502 Park Avenue
New York, New York 10022
Tel: (212) 546 1092
Fax: (212) 980 7845
Sandra Joys, *Director*

Christie's Great Estates
1850 Old Pecos Trail, Suite D
Santa Fe, NM 87505
Tel: (505) 983 8733
Fax: (505) 982 0348
Kay Coughlin, *President*

Christie's Images
13-06 43rd Avenue
Long Island City, New York 11101
Tel: (718) 472 5030
Fax: (718) 472 9005
E-mail: chrisimage@earthlink.net
Website:
www.christies.com/christiesimages/
Peter Rohowsky, *Managing Director*

Representatives

Atlanta
Alison M. Thompson
P.O. Box 550652
Atlanta, Georgia 30355
Tel: (404) 846 0780
Fax: (404) 846 0790

Baltimore/Washington, D.C.
Tel: (202) 333 7459
Fax: (202) 342 0537

Boston/New England
Elizabeth M. Chapin
Susan Florence, *Jewelry*
Brigitte Bradford, *International Rep.*
216 Newbury Street
Boston, Massachusetts 02116-2543
Tel: (617) 536 6000
Fax: (617) 536 0002

Chicago/Midwest
Gary Piattoni
Mary Ahern
Laura de Frise
Frances Blair
Susan Florence, *Jewelry*
875 N. Michigan Ave., Suite 3810
Chicago, Illinois 60611-1803
Tel: (312) 787 2765
Fax: (312) 951 7449
Toll Free (877) 787 0001
(outside Illinois)

Dallas
Carolyn Foxworth
5500 Preston Road, Suite 210
Dallas, Texas 75205
Tel: (214) 521 1843
Fax: (214) 521 8265

Delaware
Andrew C. Rose
P.O. Box 4357
Greenville, Delaware 19807
Tel: (302) 421 5719
Fax: (302) 421 5719

Houston
Lisa Cavanaugh
5900 Memorial Drive
Suite 203
Houston, Texas 77007
Tel: (713) 802 0191
Fax: (713) 802 0193

Miami
Vivian Pfeiffer
Susan Florence, *Jewelry*
Jean Kislak, *International Rep.*
Alina Pedroso Arellano,
International Rep.
110 Merrick Way, Suite 2A
Coral Gables, Florida 33134
Tel: (305) 445 1487
Fax: (305) 441 6561

Minneapolis
Kelly Perry
Carol Bemis, *Consultant*
706 Second Avenue South
Suite 710
Minneapolis, Minnesota 55402
Tel: (612) 664 0478
Fax: (612) 664 0479

Montgomery
Carol W. Ballard
P.O. Box 231207
Montgomery, Alabama 36123
Tel: (334) 244 9688
Fax: (334) 244 9588

New Orleans
Susan Gore Brennan
240A Chartres Street
New Orleans, Louisiana 70130
Tel: (504) 522 0008
Fax: (504) 522 8005

Newport
Betsy D. Ray
Ralph Carpenter, *Consultant*
228 Spring Street
Newport, Rhode Island 02840
Tel: (401) 849 9222
Fax: (401) 849 6322

Oklahoma City
Konrad Keesee, *International Rep.*
6421 Avondale Drive
Oklahoma City
Oklahoma 73116
Tel: (405) 843 1574
Fax: (405) 842 1775

Palm Beach
Meg Bowen
Susan Florence, *Jewelry*
Helen Cluett, *International Rep.*
440 Royal Palm Way, Suite 103
Palm Beach, Florida 33480
Tel: (561) 833 6952
Fax: (561) 833 0007

Philadelphia
Susan Ravenscroft
Paul Ingersoll, *Consultant*
P.O. Box 1112
Bryn Mawr, Pennsylvania 19010
Tel: (610) 525 5493
Fax: (610) 525 0967

San Francisco/Pacific Northwest
Laura Knoop King
400 Montgomery Street, Suite 920
San Francisco, California 94104
Tel: (415) 982 0982
Fax: (415) 982 8982

Santa Barbara
Carlyle C. Eubank
P.O. Box 1598
Santa Ynez, California 93460
Tel: 805 688 2728
Fax: 805 686 4548

Seattle
Catherine Vare
2802 East Madison Street
Suite 107
Seattle, WA 98112
Tel: (206) 323 2264
Fax: (206) 320 0725

St. Louis
Tel: (312) 787 2765
Fax: (312) 951 7449
Toll Free (877) 787 0001
(outside Illinois)

Washington, D.C./Baltimore
Cathy Sledz
Brittain Cudlip, *International Rep.*
Nuala Pell, *International Rep.*
Joan Gardner, *International Rep.*
Hamilton Court
1228 31st Street N.W.
Washington, D.C. 20007
Tel: (202) 333 7459
Fax: (202) 342 0537

Argentina
Cristina Erhart del Campo
Arroyo 850
1007 Capital
Buenos Aires, Argentina
Tel: (541) 393 4222
Fax: (541) 394 9578

Bermuda
Betsy Ray
Tel: (401) 849 9222
Fax: (401) 849 6322

Brazil
Rio de Janeiro
Candida Sodré
Maria Teresa Sodré
Rue Icatu 39, APT. 203
Rio de Janeiro 22260-190
Tel: (5521) 539 9583
Fax: (5521) 286 8237
São Paulo
Paulo Figueiredo
Maria Teresa Sozio
Alameda Casa Branca 851 cj. 24/25
01408-001 São Paulo, Brazil
Tel: (5511) 881 0435
Fax: (5511) 852 7244

Canada
Montreal
Brenda Norris, *International Rep.*
Tel: (514) 932 5134
Fax: (514) 932 5134

Toronto
Suzanne E. Davis
170 Bloor Street West, Suite 210
Toronto, Ontario M5S 1T9
Tel: (416) 960 2063
Fax: (416) 960 8815
Tel: (800) 960 2063 *(Canada)*
Vancouver
Jodi M. Norrison
555 West Hastings Street, Suite 700
Vancouver,
British Columbia V6B 4N5
Tel: (604) 605 3330
Fax: (604) 605 3331
Tel: (888) 382 9222 *(Canada)*

Chile
Denise Ratinoff de Lira
Martin de Zamora
3611 Los Condes
Santiago de Chile
Tel: (562) 231 7349
Fax: (562) 232 2671

Mexico
Patricia Hernández
Miguel Cervantes, *Consultant*
Christie's Mexico
Galileo 54, piso 2
Col. Polanco, 11560 México, D.F.
Tel: (525) 281 5503, 281 5463
Fax: (525) 281 5454

Uruguay
Cristina G. de Berenbau
Gral. French 1767
Montevideo 11500
Tel: (598) 2600 7723
Fax: (598) 2600 7723

Venezuela
Alain Jathière, *International Rep.*
Quinta las Magnolias
Calle Los Olivos
Los Chorros, Caracas
Tel: (582) 238 03 55
Fax: (582) 235 76 13

Regional Offices
Mary Hoeveler, *Director*
Monique Foster, *Regional Coordinator*
Tel: (212) 702 5496
Fax: (212) 750 6498

International Representatives
Nan Kempner, *New York*
Mary Libby, *New York*
Bonnie Stern, *New York*
Angus Wilkie, *New York*
Brigitte Bradford, *Boston*
Alina Pedroso Arellano, *Miami*
Jean Kislak, *Miami*
Helen Cluett, *Palm Beach*
Brittain Cudlip, *Washington, D.C.*
Joan Gardner, *Washington, D.C.*
Nuala Pell, *Washington, D.C.*
Konrad Keesee, *Oklahoma City*
Brenda Norris, *Montreal*
Terry Stanfill, *Los Angeles*
Alain Jathière, *Caracas*

NY 19/10/98

SALEROOMS AND REPRESENTATIVES

Asia and Pacific
Salerooms

Australia
Melbourne
The Lord Poltimore, *Chairman*
Roger McIlroy, *Managing Director*
Christie's Australia Pty. Ltd.
1 Darling Street
South Yarra, Victoria 3141
Tel: (613) 9820 4311
Fax: (613) 9820 4876

Sydney
180 Jersey Road
Woollahra, N.S.W. 2025
Tel: (612) 9326 1422
Fax: (612) 9327 8439

Hong Kong
Anthony Lin, *Managing Director*
Ben Kong, *Chinese Paintings*
Edmond Chin, *Western & Jadeite Jewelry*
Christie's Hong Kong Ltd.
2203–5 Alexandra House
16–20 Chater Road, Central
Hong Kong
Tel: (852) 2521 5396
Fax: (852) 2845 2646

Singapore
Irene Lee, *Managing Director*
Cecilia Ong, *Consultant*
Christie's International Singapore
Pte Ltd.
Unit 3, Parklane,
Goodwood Park Hotel
22 Scotts Road, Singapore 228221
Tel: (65) 235 3828
Fax: (65) 235 8128

Worldwide
Representatives

Asia Regional Office
Anthony Lin, *Deputy Chairman*
Philip Ng, *Managing Director, Asia*
501 Orchard Road
15-02 Wheelock Place
Singapore 238880
Tel: (65) 737 3884
Fax: (65) 733 7975

Australia
Adelaide
James and Ian Bruce
444-446 Pulteney Street
Adelaide S.A. 5000
Tel: (618) 8232 2860
Fax: (618) 8232 6506

Brisbane
Nicole Roberts
1st Floor
482 Brunswick Street
Fortitude Valley
Queensland 4006
Tel: (617) 3254 1499
Fax: (617) 3254 1566

Perth
Cherry Lewis
68 Mount Street
Perth WA 6000
Tel: (618) 9321 5764
Fax: (618) 9322 1387

People's Republic of China
Beijing
Lillian Chin
Christie, Manson & Woods Ltd.
16B CITIC Building
19 Jianguomenwai Dajie
Beijing 100004
China
Tel: (8610) 6500 6517
Fax: (8610) 6500 6034

Shanghai
Lillian Chin
Christie's Shanghai Limited
Suite 404
Shanghai Centre
1376 Nanjing Road West
Shanghai 200040
Tel: (8621) 6279 8773
Fax: (8621) 6279 8771

India
Amrita Jhaveri
Christie's Bombay
3 Shelleys Estate
30 P. J. Ramchandani Marg
Mumbai 400-039
Tel: (91 22) 285 5649
Fax: (91 22) 288 1387
Rohni Khosla *(Consultant)*
Tel: (91 11) 687 4316
Fax: (91 11) 687 4316

Indonesia
Jakarta
Mrs. Deborah Iskandar
Christie, Manson & Woods Ltd.
The Regent Jakarta
Jl Rasuna Said
Jakarta 12920
Indonesia
Tel: (6221) 527 2606
Fax: (6221) 527 2605

Japan
Sachiko Hibiya,
President
Roddy Ropner,
Managing Director
Christie's Japan Limited
Sankyo Ginza Bldg. 4F
6-5-13 Ginza,
Chuo-ku, Tokyo 104-0061
Tel: (813) 3571 0668
Fax: (813) 3571 5853

Lebanon
Beirut
P.O. Box 11-3252
Beirut
Tel: (96) 11 737 859
Fax: (96) 11 737 860

Malaysia
Lim Meng Hong
Tunku Zahiah Sulong, *Consultant*
Christie Manson & Woods Ltd
Lobby-Unit 2 Renaissance Hotel
Jalan Sultan Ismail
Kuala Lumpur 50450
Malaysia
Tel: (603) 266 6300
Fax: (603) 266 3630

South Africa
Cape Town
Juliet Lomberg
14 Hillwood Road
Claremont
Cape Town 7700
Tel: (2721) 761 2676
Fax: (2721) 762 7129

Durban
Gillian Scott-Berning
P.O. Box 50227
Musgrave Road
Durban 4062
Tel: (2731) 207 8427
Fax: (2731) 207 8427

Johannesburg
Harriet Hedley
P.O. Box 72126
Parkview
Johannesburg 2122
Tel: (2711) 486 0967
Fax: (2711) 646 0390

South Korea
Mrs. Shin Duk Young
Christie's Korea
Hotel Shilla, 5F
202, 2-Ga, Jangchung-Dong
Chung-ku
Seoul, 100-392 Korea
Tel: (82) 2 230 3139
Fax: (82) 2 230 3138

Taiwan
Anthony Lin, *Managing Director*
Nancy Chen, *General Manager*
Christie's Hong Kong Ltd.
Taiwan Branch
13/F. No. 207 Tun Hua South Road
sec. 2, Suite 1302
Taipei, Taiwan
Tel: (8862) 2736 3356
Fax: (8862) 2736 4856

SALEROOMS AND REPRESENTATIVES

UNITED KINGDOM
SALEROOMS
HEAD OFFICE
King Street :–
Christie, Manson & Woods Ltd.
8 King Street, St. James's
London SW1Y 6QT
Tel: (0171) 839 9060
Fax: (0171) 839 1611
Christopher Balfour, *Chairman*
François Curiel, *Vice Chairman*
John Lumley, *Vice Chairman*
Maria Reinshagen, *Vice Chairman*
The Earl of Halifax, *Vice Chairman*
Charles Cator, *Deputy Chairman*
Anthony Streatfeild, *Deputy Chairman*
The Lord Poltimore, *Deputy Chairman*
Edward Dolman, *Managing Director*

South Kensington :–
Christie's South Kensington Ltd.
85 Old Brompton Road
London SW7 3LD
Tel: (0171) 581 7611
Fax: (0171) 321 3321
W.A. Coleridge, F.R.I.C.S. *President*
D.M.C. Chichester, *Chairman*
P.A. Barthaud, *Managing Director*

Scotland
Glasgow :–
Christie's Scotland Ltd.
164-166 Bath Street, Glasgow G2 4TB
Tel: (0141) 332 8134
Fax: (0141) 332 5759
D.M.C. Chichester, *Chairman*
P. Arbuthnot, *Managing Director*

Other Services

Christie's Education
63 Old Brompton Road
London SW7 3JS
Tel: (0171) 581 3933
Fax: (0171) 589 0383
Irmgard Pickering, *Managing Director*

Christie's Fine Art
Security Services Limited
42 Ponton Road
Nine Elms
London SW8 5BA
Tel: (0171) 622 0609
Fax: (0171) 978 2073
Gordon Brennan-Jesson
Colin Reeve
Sydney Gill

Christie's Images
1 Langley Lane
London SW8 1TH
Tel: (0171) 582 1282
Fax: (0171) 582 5632
E-mail: cImage@Compuserve.com
Website:
www.christies.com/christiesimages/
Shaunagh Money-Coutts,
Managing Director
Camilla Young, *Manager*

England & Wales
REPRESENTATIVES
SOUTH EAST

South East Area Office
Sussex & Surrey
• Mark Wrey
North Street
Petworth
West Sussex GU28 0DD
Tel: (01798) 344440
Fax: (01798) 344442

Hampshire & Berkshire
Richard Wills
Middleton Estate Office
Longparish, Andover
Hampshire SP11 6PL
Tel: (01264) 720211
Fax: (01264) 720271

Kent
‡Christopher Proudfoot
The Old Rectory
Fawkham, Longfield
Kent DA3 8LX
Tel: (01474) 702854
Fax: (01474) 702854

Mrs. Gail Jessel
Ladham House
Goudhurst
Kent TN17 1DB
Tel: (01580) 212 595
Fax: (01580) 212 596

SOUTH WEST
South West Area Office

West Country and Wiltshire
• Richard de Pelet
Huntsman's Lodge, Inwood
Templecombe, Somerset BA8 0PF
Tel: (01963) 370518
Fax: (01963) 370605

South Dorset & South Hampshire
Nigel Thimbleby
Wolfeton House, Nr. Dorchester
Dorset DT2 9QN
Tel: (01305) 268748
Fax: (01305) 265090

Devon & Cornwall
The Hon. George Lopes, A.R.I.C.S.
Gnaton Estate Office
Yealmpton, Plymouth
Devon PL8 2HU
Tel: (01752) 880636
Fax: (01752) 880968

CENTRAL & EASTERN
Central & Eastern Area Office

South Midlands & South Wales
• The Earl Fortescue
Simon Reynolds
111 The Promenade
Cheltenham, Glos. GL50 1PS
Tel: (01242) 518999
Fax: (01242) 576240

East Midlands
Rupert Hanbury
The Old Dairy
Elton
Peterborough PE8 6SQ
Tel: (01832) 280 876
Fax: (01832) 280 877
*Mrs. William Proby

East Anglia
◇Charles Bingham-Newland
Sackville Place
44-48 Magdalen Street
Norwich NR3 1JU
Tel: (01603) 614546
Fax: (01603) 618176
*Thomas Fellowes

Essex & Hertfordshire
James Service
Hawkins Harvest
Great Bardfield
Essex CM7 4QW
Tel: (01371) 810189
Fax: (01371) 810028

NORTH
North Area Office

North-West Midlands
& North Wales
• Richard Roundell, F.R.I.C.S.
Jane Blood
Dorfold Hall, Nantwich
Cheshire CW5 8LD
Tel: (01270) 627 024
Fax: (01270) 628 723

Yorkshire
◇Thomas Scott, F.S.A. (Scot)
Stephanie Bilton
*Sir Nicholas Brooksbank, Bt.
Princes House
13 Princes Square, Harrogate,
North Yorkshire HG1 1LW
Tel: (01423) 509 699
Fax: (01423) 509 977
*Richard Compton

North West
Victor Gubbins, F.R.I.C.S.
Eden Lacey, Lazonby, Penrith
Cumbria CA10 1BZ
Tel: (01768) 898 800
Fax: (01768) 898 020

Northumbria
Aidan Cuthbert
Eastfield House, Main Street
Corbridge
Northumberland, NE45 5LA
Tel: (01434) 633181
Fax: (01434) 633891

Nottingham & Derbyshire
David Coke-Steel
Trusley Old Hall
Sutton-on-the-Hill
Ashbourne
Derbyshire DE6 5JG
Tel: (01283) 733783
Fax: (01283) 733076

Scotland
REPRESENTATIVES

Edinburgh & the Borders
Bernard Williams
Robert Lagneau
5 Wemyss Place
Edinburgh EH3 6DH
Tel: (0131) 225 4756/7
Fax: (0131) 225 1723

North of Scotland
Lady Eliza Leslie Melville
Lochluichart Lodge
By Garve
Ross-shire IV23 2PZ
Tel: (01997) 414370
Fax: (01997) 414340

South West Scotland
Charlotte Dickie
Poundland, Moniaive
Dumfriesshire DG3 4EG
Tel: (01848) 200 730
Fax: (01848) 200 731

Tayside, Fife & Grampian
Bernard Williams
Robert Lagneau
3/5 Mill Street
Perth PH1 5JB
Tel: (01738) 643088
Fax: (01738) 635227

IRELAND
Belfast
◇Danny Kinahan
Templepatrick
Co. Antrim BT39 0AH
Tel: (01849) 433480
Fax: (01849) 433410

Glin
Desmond Fitz-Gerald, Knight of Glin
Glin Castle
Glin, Co. Limerick
Fax: (00353) 683 4364
52 Waterloo Road
Dublin 4
(Private Residence)
Tel: (00353) 1 668 0585
Fax: (00353) 1 668 0271

CHANNEL ISLANDS
Melissa Bonn
Richard de la Hey
58 David Place, St. Helier
Jersey
Tel: (01534) 877582
Fax: (01534) 877540

ISLE OF MAN
The Marchioness Conyngham
Myrtle Hill, Andreas Road
Ramsey, Isle of Man IM8 3UA
Tel: (01624) 814502
Fax: (01624) 814502

NY 30/7/98

Europe
Salerooms

Greece

Athens
Elisavet Logotheti-Lyra,
Managing Director
Christie's Hellas Ltd.
26 Philellinon Street
10558 Athens
Tel: (301) 324 6900
Fax: (301) 324 6925

Israel
Mary Gilben
Christie's (Israel) Limited
Asia House, 4 Weizmann Street
Tel Aviv 64239
Tel: (9723) 6950695
Fax: (9723) 6952751

Italy

Rome
Franz Ziegler, *Managing Director*
Francesco Alverà
Christie's (International) S.A.,
Palazzo Massimo Lancellotti
Piazza Navona 114, Rome 00186
Tel: (3906) 687 2787
Fax: (3906) 686 9902
(3906) 689 3080

Monaco
Pascal Bégo
Christie's Monaco S.A.M.
Park Palace, 98000 Monte-Carlo
Tel: (377) 97 97 11 00
Fax: (377) 97 97 11 01

The Netherlands

Amsterdam
Bernard Steyaert, *Managing Director*
Christie's Amsterdam B.V.
Cornelis Schuytstraat 57,
1071 JG Amsterdam
Tel: (3120) 57 55 255
Fax: (3120) 66 40 899

Switzerland

Geneva
François Curiel, *President*
Elisabeth Storm Nagy, *Vice President*
Franz Ziegler, *Managing Director*
Christie's (International) S.A.,
8 Place de la Taconnerie
1204 Geneva
Tel: (41 22) 319 17 66
Fax: (41 22) 319 17 67

Zurich
Maria Reinshagen,
Vice Chairman Christie's Europe
Dr. Brigit Bernegger, *Vice President*
Claudia Steinfels, *General Manager*
Christie's (Int.) A.G.
Steinwiesplatz, 8032 Zürich
Tel: (411) 268 1010
Fax: (411) 268 1011

Other Services
Christie's Education

France
Hôtel Salomon de Rothschild
11 Rue Berryer, 75008 Paris
Tel: (331) 42 25 10 90
Fax: (331) 42 25 10 91

Europe
Representatives

Austria
Dr. Johanna Schönburg-Hartenstein
Cornelia Pallavicini, *Managing Director*
Christie's Kunstauktionen GmbH
Bankgasse 1/Herrengasse 17
1010 Vienna
Tel: (431) 533 88 12
Fax: (431) 533 71 66

Belgium
Bernard Steyaert, *Chairman*
Bernard de Launoit, *Managing Director*
Géraldine André, *Contemporary Art*
Roland de Lathuy, *Old Master Pictures*
Christie's Belgium S.A.
33 Boulevard de Waterloo
1000 Brussels
Tel: (322) 512 8830
Fax: (322) 513 3279

Czech Republic
HSH The Princess Elisabeth Lobkowicz
Snemovni Ulice 11
Mala Strana, 11800 Praha-1
Czech Republic
Tel: (42-02) 57 09 61 27
Fax: (42-02) 57 09 61 28

Denmark
Birgitta Hillingsø
Dronningens Tværgade 10
1302 Copenhagen K
Tel: (45) 33 32 70 75
Fax: (45) 33 13 00 75

Finland
Barbro Schauman
Christie's
Vuorimiehenkatu 5A, 00140 Helsinki
Tel: (3589) 60 82 12
Fax: (3589) 66 06 87

France

Aix-en-Provence
Fabienne Albertini
28 rue Lieutaud, 13100
Aix en Provence
Tel: (33) 4 92 72 43 31
Fax: (33) 4 92 72 53 65

Bordeaux
Marie-Cecile Moueix
49 Cours Xavier Arnozan
33000 Bordeaux
Tel: (33) 5 56 81 65 47
Fax: (33) 5 56 51 15 71

Centre et Val de Loire
Nicole de Yturbe
Château de Montgraham
28400 Souance au Perche
Tel: (33) 2 37 29 13 66

Lyon
Vicomte Thierry de Lachaise
36 Place Bellecour
69002 Lyon
Tel: (33) 4 78 42 83 82
Fax: (33) 4 78 42 83 84

Paris
Hubert de Givenchy, *President*
Hugues Joffre, *President du Directoire*
Bertrand du Vignaud
Franck Prazan
Christie's France S.A.
6 Rue Paul Baudry, 75008 Paris
Tel: (33) 1 40 76 85 85
Fax: (33) 1 42 56 26 01

Germany
Dr. Johann Georg Prinz von
Hohenzollern, *Non Executive Chairman*
Jörg-Michael Bertz, *Deputy Chairman*
Stefan Prinz von Ratibor,
General Manager
Birgid Seynsche-Vautz,
Administrative Manager

Berlin
Stefan Prinz von Ratibor,
General Manager
Marianne Kewenig
Victoria von Specht
Frederik Schwarz, *Jewellery*
Fasanenstraße 72, 10719 Berlin
Tel: (4930) 885 695 0
Fax: (4930) 885 695 95

Düsseldorf
Jörg-Michael Bertz, *Senior Specialist*
(19th and 20th Century Pictures)
Brigid Seynsche-Vautz,
Administrative Manager
Maike Borgwardt
Valuation Manager
Christie's (Deutschland) GmbH
P.O. Box 101810, Inselstraße 15
40479 Düsseldorf
Tel: (49211) 491 5930
Fax: (49211) 492 0339

Frankfurt
Charlotte Prinzessin von Croy
Gerard Goodrow
Nina von Oudarza
Arndtstraße 18
60325 Frankfurt am Main
Tel: (4969) 74 50 21
Fax: (4969) 75 20 79

Hamburg
Christiane Gräfin zu Rantzau
Wentzelstraße 21, 22301 Hamburg
Tel: (4940) 279 4073
Fax: (4940) 270 4497

Munich
Marie Christine Gräfin Huyn
Residenzstraße 27, 80333 München
Tel: (4989) 22 95 39
Fax: (4989) 29 63 02

Stuttgart
Claudia Freiin von Saint-Andre
Relenbergstrasse 69, 70174 Stuttgart
Tel: (49711) 226 9699
Fax: (49711) 226 0607

Greece

Thessaloniki
Christie's Thessaloniki
Aristotelous 8, 546 23 Thessaloniki
Tel: (3031) 244607
Fax: (3031) 242931

Italy

Florence
Alessandra Niccolini di Camugliano
Casella Postale 62
56038 Ponsacco (PI)
Tel: (39587) 735487
Fax: (39587) 735487

Genoa
Rachele Guicciardi
Via Belvedere Montaldo, 5
16124 Genoa
Tel: (3910) 247 1204
Fax: (3910) 246 5351

Milan
Clarice Pecori Giraldi
Director Business Development
Franz Ziegler
Domenico Filipponi, *General Manager*
Christie's (Int.) S.A.
Piazza Santa Maria delle Grazie 1
20123 Milano
Tel: (3902) 46 70 141
Fax: (3902) 46 70 1429

Lazio
Alessandra Allaria
Via Cassiodoro 14, 00193 Rome
Tel: (396) 687 4147
Fax: (396) 683 2442

Turin
Sandro Perrone di San Martino
Via Maria Vittoria 4, 10123 Turin
Tel: (3911) 561 9453
Fax: (3911) 542 710

Veneto
Bianca Arrivabene Valenti Gonzaga
Casella Postale 602
30100 Venezia Centrale
Tel: (3941) 277 0086
Fax: (3941) 277 0086

Luxembourg
Countess Marina von Kamarowsky
16 rue Wurth-Paquet
2737 Luxembourg
Tel: (352) 44 04 95
Fax: (352) 44 04 92

The Netherlands

Bloemendaal
PO Box 116
2060 AC Bloemendaal
Tel: (3123) 526 0658
Fax: (3123) 526 0658

Rotterdam
PO Box 4019, 3006 AA Rotterdam
Tel: (3110) 212 0553
Fax: (3110) 212 0553

Norway
Benedicte Løvenskiold Dyvik
Christie's
Colbjørnsengst, 1, N-0256 Oslo 2
Tel: (4722) 44 12 42
Fax: (4722) 55 92 36

Portugal
Mafalda Pereira Coutinho
Rua da Lapa 67, 1200 Lisbon
Tel: (3511) 396 9750
Fax: (3511) 396 9732

Spain

Barcelona
Piru Cantarell de Andreu
Mallorca, 235, 08008 Barcelona
Tel: (34) 9 34 87 82 59
Fax: (34) 9 34 87 85 04

Madrid
Casilda Fz-Villaverde y Silva
Pablo Melendo
Christie's Iberica S.L.
Antonio Maura 10, 28014 Madrid
Tel: (34) 9 15 32 66 26/7
Fax: (34) 9 15 23 12 40

Sweden

Stockholm
Lillemor Malmström
Sturegatan 26, 11436 Stockholm
Tel: (468) 662 0131
Fax: (468) 660 0725

South of Sweden
Baroness Irma Silfverschiold
230 41 Klagerup
Tel: (4640) 44 03 60
Fax: (4640) 44 03 71

South west of Sweden
Susanne Wiklund,
Forsvarsgatan 12
426 76 Vastra Frolunda, Gothenburg
Tel: (4631) 69 40 68
Fax: (4631) 694530

Switzerland

Lugano
Manoli Traxler
Christie's (Int.) S.A.
via soave, 9, 6900 Lugano
Tel: (4191) 922 2031
Fax: (4191) 922 2032

Geneve – see Salerooms
Zurich – see Salerooms

All photography is produced by Christie's in-house photographers.

Catalogue produced by Vauxhall Pre Press, 21-25 South Lambeth Road, London SW8 1SX Tel: (0171) 582 1188
Printed in England